Quo Vadimus?

E. B. WHITE

QUO VADIMUS?

OR
THE CASE FOR THE BICYCLE

Harper & Brothers Publishers
New York and London

QUO VADIMUS?

To

Walt Whitman, of Paumanok; Grover Whalen,
of Flushing Bay; and the openers of time capsules
in the world of tomorrow.

*"Only a few hints—a few diffused, faint clues
and indirections . . ."*

CONTENTS

*

CONTENTS

I. Parables and Prophecies

The Wings of Orville

ALL THROUGH THE COURTSHIP, THE BUILDING OF the nest, and even the incubation of the eggs, Orville had acted in what to the hen sparrow seemed a normal manner. He had been fairly attentive, too, as cock birds go. The first indication Orville's wife had of any quirk in his nature came one morning when he turned up before breakfast carrying a ginger-ale bottle-cap in his beak.

"I won't be home for lunch," he said. His mate looked at the bottle-cap.

"What's that for?"

Orville tried to act preoccupied, but it wasn't a success. He knew he'd better make a direct answer. "Well," he said, "I'm going to fly to Hastings-upon-Hudson and back, carrying this bottle-cap."

The hen looked at him. "What's the idea of carrying a bottle-cap up the river and back?"

"It's a flight," replied Orville, importantly.

"What do you mean, it's a *flight*? How else would you get there if you didn't fly?"

"Well, this is different," said Orville. "I want to

prove the practicability of a round-trip flight between Madison Square and Hastings-upon-Hudson carrying a bottle-cap."

There wasn't anything she could say to that. Orville stayed around for a few minutes, then, after what seemed to his wife a great deal of unnecessary fluttering on the edge of the nest, he gripped the bottle-cap firmly in his bill and departed. She noticed that he was flying faster than his usual gait, and was keeping an unusually straight course. Dutifully she watched him out of sight. "He'll be all tuckered out when he gets back," she thought to herself.

Orville, as the hen sparrow had expected, was tired that evening; but he seemed pleased with the results of the day.

"How did it go?" asked his wife, after he had deposited the bottle-cap on the base of the statue of Admiral Farragut.

"Fine," said Orville. "I ran into a little rain the other side of Yonkers, but kept right on into fair weather again. It was only bad once, when ice began to form on my wings."

His wife looked at him intently. "I don't believe for a minute," she said, "that any ice started to form on your wings."

"Yes, it did," replied Orville.

He mooched about the nest for a while, and went into a few details for the benefit of his three children.

The nest occupied by Orville's family was in a tree in Madison Square near the Farragut statue. It was no neater than most sparrows' nests, and had been constructed eagerly of a wide variety of materials, including a kite-string that hung down. One morning, a few days after the Hastings affair, Orville came to his wife with a question. "Are you through with that string?" he asked, nodding toward the trailing strand.

"Are you crazy?" she replied, sadly.

"I need it for something."

His wife gazed at him. "You're going to wreck the nest if you go pulling important strings out."

"I can get it out without hurting anything," said Orville. "I want it for a towline."

"A what?"

"Listen," said Orville, "I'm going to fly to 110th Street tomorrow, towing a wren."

The hen sparrow looked at him in disgust. "Where are you going to get a wren?"

"I can get a wren," he said, wisely. "It's all arranged. I'm going to tow it till we get up about

three thousand feet and then I'm going to cut the
wren loose and it will glide down to a landing. I
think I can prove the feasibility of towing a wren
behind a sparrow."

Orville's wife did not say anything more. Grudg-
ingly she helped him pull the kite-string from the
nest. Pretty strange doings, it seemed to her.

That evening Orville experimented alone with
his string, tying it first to one foot and then the
other. Next morning he was up at the crack of
dawn and had the string all lashed to his right leg
before breakfast. Putting in the half hitches had
occasioned an immense lot of kicking around and
had been fairly uncomfortable for the youngsters.

"For goodness' sake, Orville," said the hen sparrow, "can't you take it down to the ground and tie
it on there?"

"Do me a favor," said Orville. "Put your finger
on this knot while I draw it tight."

When the towline was arranged to his complete
satisfaction, he flew down to the Square. There he
immediately became the centre of attention. His
wife, noticing how other birds gathered around,
was a bit piqued to see all this fuss made over Orville. Sparrows, she told herself, will gape at any-

thing queer. She didn't believe that Orville had actually located a wren, and was genuinely surprised when one showed up—a tiny brown bird, with sharp eyes and a long, excitable tail. Orville greeted the wren cordially, hopping briskly round and round dragging the line. When about fifty sparrows and pigeons had congregated, he took the wren to one side. "I don't want to take off," he said, "till we get a weather report."

The news that the flight was to be delayed pending a report on weather conditions increased the interest of the other birds, and one of them volunteered to fly up to Central Park and back to find out how things were. He was back in ten minutes, and said the weather was clear. Orville, without any hesitation, motioned to the wren, who seized the towline in its beak, spread its wings rigidly, and waited. Then, at a signal from Orville, they both ran as fast as they could along the grass and jumped wildly into the air, Orville beating his wings hard. One foot, two feet, three feet off the ground they soared. Orville was working like a horse. He put everything he had into it, but soon it became clear that they hadn't enough altitude to clear a park bench that loomed up directly ahead—

and the crash came. Orville landed with the string tangled in one wing, and the wren fell to the ground, stunned.

No further attempt to tow a wren was made that day. Orville felt sick, and so did the wren. The incident, however, was the talk of the Square, and the other birds were still discussing it when night fell. When Orville's wife settled herself on the roosting branch beside her mate for the twittering vespers, she turned to him and said: "I believe you could have made it, Orville, if that darn bench hadn't been there."

"Sure we could have."

"Are you going to try again tomorrow?" There was a note of expectation in her voice.

"Yes."

The hen sparrow settled herself comfortably beside him. He, if any sparrow could, would prove the feasibility of towing a wren. For a minute she roosted there, happily. Then, when Orville had dropped off to sleep, she stole quietly down to the kitchen and busied herself making two tiny sandwiches, which she tied up in wax paper.

"I'll give him these tomorrow," she murmured, "just before he takes off."

Dr. Vinton

THE SEA PLEASED DR. VINTON AS NO OTHER SINGLE
element ever had. He was up very early the first
morning of the voyage, all shaved and dressed and
ready before the room stewards had finished wip-
ing down the corridors. It was a calm morning, a
steady morning, and the alleyways were humming
with the faint note of progress that always fills a
ship. Dr. Vinton was gratified to discover a calm
sea through his porthole, and when he stepped
forth from his state-room he was glad to find men
already at work.

This feeling of satisfaction, of benignity, ex-
tended outward toward the world and toward his
fellow men. "Cleaning her up, eh?" he said, passing one of the stewards. Fraternization was good
at any hour: it was particularly pleasing to Dr.
Vinton before breakfast. He was glad, too, that he
had remembered to refer to the ship as "her." A
pleasant conceit, making a ship feminine, he
thought.

The forward deck was still wet when he stepped

forth, but not so wet as to displease him. Spots of
it were drying in the sun, and that gave promise of
a fair, dry day, and of warm weather. The sea was
a shining expanse of lovely blue in which the sun
had already begun to cut a bright track. And the
sea, by this time, was Dr. Vinton's favorite
element.

At the moment the only other occupant of the
deck was the ship's cat, which had made a quick
trip to the scuppers and was on its way back to the
forecastle, treading gingerly the wet path. "How
free the sea stretches out!" said the Doctor, aloud.
"Like the thoughts of Man. Like *my* thoughts on
this morning," he added. No one heard him. The
look-out in the crow's nest saw him, but assumed
he had come on deck to be sick. A gull swung low
to the water. "Graceful, tireless, free," said Dr.
Vinton.

His admiration of the gull became suddenly
confused with his appreciation of his own words.
Graceful, tireless, free. Those words might well be
the outline of a sermon. Dr. Vinton tried to dis-
miss the thought, but it stuck. Graceful, tireless,
free—he could visualize the way the sermon would
work out: there would be five minutes of introduc-

tion (a word picture of a beautiful morning at sea), then he'd bring in the gull as an example to Man, graceful (grace is beauty and our lives must be beautiful), tireless (tireless in the service of the Master), free (free of the bonds of temptation and sin). "Oh my friends . . ." said Dr. Vinton to the ship's cat, just as it disappeared below.

All things seemed to be conspiring to put the Doctor into as fine a mood as he had ever experienced. There was just enough motion to the ship to suggest a mysterious buoyancy. He read the name of the ship painted on a life preserver. Amaryllis. What a pretty name! A ship that was a flower. Dr. Vinton breathed deeply of the air that was all about him in inexhaustible quantities.

A slight scraping noise attracted his attention and he looked up to where a sailor was painstakingly cleaning the brass worm-gear of a lifeboat davit, so it wouldn't jam. The sailor's neck and face were a fine red color; the lifeboat was white; the worm-gear was beginning to shine in the sun. The whole scene seemed pleasant to Dr. Vinton, although it is doubtful if he caught its utilitarian significance. "Shining her up, eh?" he called, cheerily. The sailor paused an instant, made no reply, then rubbed again. "The sea," wrote Dr. Vinton in his diary that night, "makes men silent."

Breakfast was a continuation and a heightening of the bodily and spiritual well-being that had come over the Doctor. He not only enjoyed the food, but he revelled in his ability to eat it; for he had come aboard with an abundant faith in God but with a certain dark fear of indigestion. Now it was clear that there was nothing to be afraid of. He liked the ship's coffee, and while sipping it recounted to the others at table the experiences of early morning—how pleasant it had been on deck while things were still wet and fresh with the new day, how he had seen a gull, how graceful and tire-less it was (he did not mention how free it was, he thought he would save that one), and how the sailors were out early, shining the ship. Then he took another cup of coffee.

Dr. Vinton spent most of the morning forward, watching the sea. He noticed the look-out, and once, when a ship was sighted off the starboard bow, he saw the look-out report it to the bridge with a pull on the bell lanyard. That pleased him. The eyes of a ship, he thought. Always watching,

in fog, in rain, in storm. He told his table com-
panions about it later in the dining saloon, referring to the look-out as "the outlook." In the
afternoon he played shuffleboard on the sunny
boat-deck with Mrs. Lamont, from Nyack, and
won. He could not recall ever having had a period
of such sustained good feeling, such serenity. Not
even when he spoke sharply to a sailor who was
reprimanding a little boy for throwing rubber
quoits rapidly into the sea, did he lose his mellow
humor. "You must remember," he said to the
sailor, smiling, "that he is just a little boy." The
sailor made no answer and again Dr. Vinton made
a mental note that the sea makes men silent.

The Amaryllis was a modern ship. Fans sucked
in air through ventilators and cooled every cabin
with a forced draught. Dr. Vinton noticed with
pleasure that, go where he would, he was gently
followed by a little stream of fresh air. He noticed
it particularly when he went to his state-room to
clean up for dinner and sat on the lounge for
a moment, resting. The air came whispering
through a small hole in the air shaft and bathed
his face, refreshingly. Somehow this little draught
of air seemed to epitomize human progress to him.

It was no longer necessary to endure the discomforts of the unenlightened past. How far we had come from the slave ships of Roman days! We were free, not only of chains, we were free of unpleasantly hot state-rooms; we were coming to be a more graceful, tireless, free race of people. Nor did Dr. Vinton regard this new freedom entirely from a selfish point of view; he thought of the men tending the burners in the engine room below, and of how they too were cooled by a forced draught, and he was glad for them. He enjoyed dinner.

The next day was a repetition of his good feeling, and he found good in everything. The day after that was equally pleasant. On the evening of the third day, however, the Amaryllis ran into a heavy fog at ten-thirty o'clock, struck an iceberg, and sank with all on board—which was the first untoward incident of the entire voyage for Dr. Vinton.

I say sank with all on board—that is not precisely the case. Through an interesting circumstance Dr. Vinton did not go down with the ship. When the disaster occurred he was in the main social hall where the ship's concert was going on, an entertainment got up by the passengers. Dr. Vinton, much to his delight, had been chosen master of ceremonies for the occasion—"a rather signal honor" was the way he had expressed it in his diary. In his introductory speech he had stressed the point of friendship on shipboard, which he said was the keynote of this little gathering. "I look upon this fortunate gathering," he said, "as a sort of clearing house for friendship. I always think of a ship as a place where lasting friendships are made. I notice that our good purser has instructed each of us to apply for landing cards, that we may properly go ashore on our arrival overseas; but if *I* were the king or the president of a country, I think I should require each visitor to present a card testifying that he, or she, had made at least one *lasting friendship* whilst aboard ship." Dr. Vinton smiled, and then introduced little Virginia Marsh, aged nine, who danced. After a few other numbers Mrs. Lamont sang "The Valley of Laughter." "I am sure," said Dr. Vinton, rising to his feet, "that we have all enjoyed Mrs. Lamont's singing of this beautiful song and that she will sleep extra soundly tonight for having given all of us so much pleasure." He smiled graciously at

Mrs. Lamont and then announced that a plate would be passed, everyone being urged to contribute something, however small, to the Seamen's Institute.

It was just ten-thirty when the tin collection plate was returned, full of money, to Dr. Vinton. The Amaryllis was steaming along through the gathering fog; but the fog was not apparent in the brightly-lighted social hall, and hence it had not displeased the Doctor. Holding the plate in both hands, he turned again to the audience. "Let us sing *Auld Lang Syne*," he said, "and then swing naturally into *America*." At this moment the Amaryllis struck the iceberg and sank.

The force of the collision threw Dr. Vinton through a large porthole, and he landed on a life-raft which had broken loose at the impact and fallen into the sea. It was such a neat piece of business that it scarcely even hurt Dr. Vinton (merely a slight jar to his haunches) and would not indeed have hurt him at all had his hands been free to help break the fall. His hands still clutched the collection plate. It was all so neat that only one dollar bill was lost from the plate, and Dr. Vinton immediately replaced this with a dollar from his own pocket. Then he noticed that the ship had sunk, and that it was quite foggy. "I had better pray," he said; and he did, sitting cross-legged and quite alone in the middle of the ocean. It was the first time he had ever prayed sitting cross-legged, and it seemed both uncomfortable and disrespectful. He prayed for about an hour, and then slept.

Next morning he was up early. Although he could not shave or dress, he made a few minor adjustments to his attire and ate a peppermint, which Mrs. Lamont had given him and which he had put away in a pocket because he did not like peppermints. The fog had lifted from the sea, and Dr. Vinton noticed that the tiny deck of his raft was drying in the sun. That rather pleased him. He also discovered that it was possible to stand upright on the raft without upsetting it—even to take a step or two. So he walked up and down, stretching his legs, and was very careful not to go too near the edge. Then he sat down again and removed all the money from the collection plate, counted it to make sure it was all there, wrapped it tidily in his handkerchief, and placed it in the inside pocket of his coat for safe keeping in the event of heavy weather.

He looked at his watch, pleased to find that it was still running. Seven-thirty. Dr. Vinton remembered having seen a notice on the bulletin board of the Amaryllis saying that clocks would be set ahead forty minutes during the night, so he set his watch ahead forty minutes, wound it, and replaced it in his pocket.

The sea was a placid blue. A few hundred feet astern of the raft Dr. Vinton noticed the iceberg which had sunk the ship. Although the berg was, of course, considerably bigger and more substantial than his raft, he made no attempt to reach it, because he thought it would be too slippery to stand on and too cold to sit on—at least that was the way icebergs had always seemed to him. But the presence of the berg, so near, so shiny, and so blue, cheered him and emphasized his own good fortune. It reminded him, naturally, of the night's disaster, and tended to help him marshal his thoughts. Certainly he could not ascribe to a mere Divine idiosyncrasy the inescapable fact of his having been honored, in a most unusual way, above all other people in the ship. They were all dead and he was alive. As a thinking man it was his duty to try and understand that, regardless of his immediate embarrassment. Possibly, he reasoned, I have been spared because of my being the person on the ship best fitted to pray for the salvation of those who have gone down. The logic of this contented him somewhat, although he found himself speculating on the inconsistencies which always seemed to shroud an omnipotent gesture. He even found himself bothered by one or two rather trite old matters: why, if Providence was so interested in the salvation of an entire passenger list as to provide them with a survivor with powers of intercession, had Providence not gone the whole hog and moved the iceberg a few yards to one side, out of the path of the ship? Mostly, he avoided such thoughts; for he knew from experience that he could not follow them through to their conclusion without impairing his general health, which, after three bracing days at sea, was very good. Prayer was a perplexing thing.

Still, thought Dr. Vinton, as long as I do not fully understand my position, I suppose the only fair thing to do is to give the passengers the benefit of the doubt. With that he prayed for those who had gone down. He prayed aloud, in a normal speaking voice, for twenty-two minutes, and no-

ticed to his satisfaction that he used several rather
fresh phrases, particularly in the subaqueous pas-
sages. Then he followed with another short prayer
for himself, for although he was comfortable on
the life-raft (which he had renamed Salvation,
printing the letters neatly on the deck with his
pencil), he felt that his position in the middle of
the Atlantic was certainly not without some peril.

This latter prayer was answered with a prompt-
ness and dispatch which did credit even to om-
nipotency. In getting to a kneeling position, the
Doctor had up-ended the collection plate with his
toe, and the sun, striking the tin plate, had shot a
bright beam of light across the sea a distance of
seven miles to where the look-out of a ship was
scanning the horizon. The look-out reported it to
the bridge, the captain immediately altered his
course, and in less than an hour Dr. Vinton had
been hauled aboard and given a drink of water.
He visited the purser's office without delay and
gave up the money in his pocket, directing that it
be turned over to the Seamen's Institute.

On his return to America, Dr. Vinton experienced a new interest in, and appreciation of, dry

land. Never had the hills, the fields, the roads
around Vintondale, seemed so pleasing to eye and
spirit. Occasionally, in the busy months that followed, his thoughts strayed back to the Amaryllis
and the sea, but at such times he was reminded
inevitably of his own good fortune and of the
unique, almost Puckish, designs of the Creator.
His memories of the first three days of the voyage
were of the most pleasant sort. And he frequently
thought about the sermon on the seagull—the outline of which he recalled perfectly—but it occurred
to him that it might be in better taste to allow a
little time to elapse before using a marine subject
in the pulpit. It was part of the Doctor's policy to
avoid all discussions of the Amaryllis incident,
either in church or out; for to discuss it at all
meant that sooner or later the conversation would
swing around to the possible significance of the
event. His escape was palpably a miracle, and Dr.
Vinton rather disliked getting mixed up in the
miracles—which were properly both ancient and
impersonal. As for the sermon on the seagull, he
waited a year, and then delivered it, one lovely
bright morning: it unfolded rhythmically, just as

he had envisioned it on deck that day—the seagull, graceful (grace is beauty and our lives must be beautiful), tireless (tireless in the service of the Master), free (free of the bonds of temptation and sin). "Oh my friends . . ." said Dr. Vinton to his congregation.

Quo Vadimus?

**A GLIMPSE INTO THE FUTURE—YOU KNOW, LIKE
IN THE SUNDAY TIMES MAGAZINE**

A MAN APPROACHING ME IN EAST THIRTY-FOURTH Street, in the thick of noon, had so queer a look in his eye, such a fudgy and fearful expression, I stopped him.

"Quo vadis?" I asked.

"You mean me?" he said, sheepishly.

"Yes, sure. Quo vadis?" I repeated. "Where the hell are you going?"

"I won't tell you, because you wouldn't understand," he replied.

"Well then," I said, "I'll put it this way: quo vadimus? Where are either of us going?"

He seemed stunned. A woman, shopping, bumped lightly against him. At length he spoke, in a clear, low, frightened voice.

"I'll tell you where I'm going. I'm on my way to the Crowbar Building, Forty-first and Park, in Pershing Square, named after General Pershing in the Grand Central zone, zone as in Zonite, because I forgot to tell Miss Cortwright to leave a note for Mr. Josefson when he comes in, telling him he should tell the engraver to vignette the halftone on page forty-three of the salesmen's instruction book that Irwain, Weasey, Weasey & Button are getting out for the Fretherby-Quigley Company, which is to go to all their salesmen on the road."

"What do the salesmen sell?" I said, quietly.

"They sell a new kind of shorthand course, called the Quigley Method of Intensive Speed-writing."

"Very good," I said. "That's just the kind of errand I imagined you to be on. As I understand it, recapitulating, you are on your way to the Crowbar Building, Forty-first and Park, in Pershing Square named after General Pershing, hero of the song, 'Many a cootie came over from France in General Pershing's underpants,' in the Grand Central zone, zone as in Zonite, because you forgot to tell Miss Cortwright to leave a note for Mr. Josefson when he comes in, telling him he should tell the engraver to vignette the halftone on page forty-three of a booklet that Irwain, Weasey, Weasey & Button are getting out for the Fretherby-

Quigley Company, instructing their salesmen how to approach people to sell the Quigley Method of Intensive Speedwriting, which in turn will enable girls like Miss Cortwright to take Mr. Josefson's dictation when he has to send a memo to the engraver telling him not to forget to vignette a halftone in a booklet telling salesmen how to sell shorthand courses. Is that correct?"

"That's where I'm going," said the man.

"Well, aren't you ashamed of yourself!" I cried.

"I don't know whether I am or not," he said, with a slight touch of indignation.

"Listen, my friend," I went on, fixing him with my eye, "all you really want is a decent meal when it comes mealtime, isn't it?"

"And a warm place to sleep when it comes night," he added quickly, almost eagerly.

"Exactly, and a warm place to sleep when it comes night. All right then, don't you think that you, who just want a decent meal when it comes mealtime, and a warm place to sleep when it comes night—don't you think you are pretty far from the main issue if you're on your way to tell a Miss Cortwright to leave a note for a Mr. Josefson telling him to . . ."

He motioned me with his hand to stop. "You

needn't go on. Yes, I'm far from the issue, sir,"
he said. "But I do not know what to do. It must be
something about the age—what do they call it, the
'machine' age? This Miss Cortwright . . . I don't
know. This Josefson . . . I don't know. Nice people, I suppose. It is all so complex. I just drifted
into it."

"Exactly," I said. "And it's getting worse, mind
you. I predict a bright future for complexity in
this country. Did it ever occur to you that there's
no limit to how complicated things can get, on
account of one thing always leading to another?
Did you ever stop to consider how the Cortwrights
lead to the Josefsons, and how the Josefsons lead
to the engravers? Paths of glory, leading to the
engravers, my man. Did you ever stop to think
what might happen if people by accident forgot
where the whole thing started?"

The man shook his head, very slightly. His eyes
were bright but out of focus. I went on, sternly.

"Only the other evening," I said, "I stopped a
man on Broadway who had in his face the same
look that I detected in *your* face a moment ago.
To him, too, I said: 'Quo vadis?' And he, too, told
me a story much like yours. He told me, my friend,

that he was on his way to see a Mr. Fitch in the Pari-Mutuel Building, who wanted to get permission to make a talking picture of an airplane towing a glider in which was seated a man listening to a radio which was receiving a colored dialogue between two men named Amos and Andy who were talking together in order to advertise a toothpaste and the name of the toothpaste was . . ."

"Pepsodent," put in my man.

"Yes, Pepsodent. And that man—all he really wanted, when you came right down to it, was a decent meal when it came mealtime."

"And a warm place to sleep when it came night," added my friend, hurriedly.

"Exactly."

There was a pause in our conversation at this point. Cars passed back and forth in the street. Women shoppers brushed lightly against us— women who were on their way to buy fringes for lampshades, women who were on their way to buy printed silk, women who were on their way to buy the hooks that hold the rods that hold the curtains. Suddenly my friend addressed me.

"Now *you* tell *me* where *you're* going!" he said, sharply.

"Ha, not on your life—you don't catch me that way," I cried. "I'm not telling you where I'm going."

"I suppose you're going fishing," said the man, smirking.

"Smirk again and I'll smack you," I said. "I always smack smirkers."

He smirked. I smacked him.

"Now ask me where I'm going!" I said, holding him by the arm.

"I bet I can guess where you're going. I bet you're a writer, on his way to write something. I know your type. You're going to write a story about 'complexity'—about meeting a man in East Thirty-fourth Street who was on his way to the Crowbar Building in Pershing Square, named after General Pershing in the Grand Central zone, zone as in Zonite, because he forgot to tell Miss Cortwright to leave a note for Mr. Josefson to tell the engraver to vignette the half-tone . . ."

"Don't repeat it," I said, breaking down. "That's exactly where I'm going."

". . . so a person like Miss Cortwright will have something to read, and not understand, when she isn't busy with dictation," he said, finishing up.

"That's it."

"And all you want is a decent meal when it comes mealtime, isn't it?" asked my friend.

"And a warm place to sleep when it comes night," I added quickly, almost eagerly.

"Sure, I know," he said. "Well, vale!"

"Vale, kid!" I replied. And we continued on our lonely and imponderable ways.

The Family Which Dwelt Apart

ON A SMALL, REMOTE ISLAND IN THE LOWER reaches of Barnetuck Bay there lived a family of fisherfolk by the name of Pruitt. There were seven of them, and they were the sole inhabitants of the place. They subsisted on canned corn, canned tomatoes, pressed duck, whole-wheat bread, terrapin, Rice Krispies, crabs, cheese, queen olives, and homemade wild-grape preserve. Once in a while Pa Pruitt made some whiskey and they all had a drink.

They liked the island and lived there from choice. In winter, when there wasn't much doing, they slept the clock around, like so many bears. In summer they dug clams and set off a few pinwheels and salutes on July 4th. No case of acute appendicitis had ever been known in the Pruitt household, and when a Pruitt had a pain in his side he never even noticed whether it was the right side or the left side, but just hoped it would go away, and it did.

One very severe winter Barnetuck Bay froze over and the Pruitt family was marooned. They

couldn't get to the mainland by boat because the
ice was too thick, and they couldn't walk ashore
because the ice was too treacherous. But inasmuch
as no Pruitt had anything to go ashore for, except mail (which was entirely second class), the
freeze-up didn't make any difference. They stayed
indoors, kept warm, and ate well, and when there
was nothing better to do, they played crokinole.
The winter would have passed quietly enough had
not someone on the mainland remembered that
the Pruitts were out there in the frozen bay. The
word got passed around the county and finally
reached the Superintendent of State Police, who
immediately notified Pathé News and the United
States Army. The Army got there first, with three
bombing planes from Langley Field, which flew
low over the island and dropped packages of dried
apricots and bouillon cubes, which the Pruitts
didn't like much. The newsreel plane, smaller
than the bombers and equipped with skis, arrived
next and landed on a snow-covered field on the
north end of the island. Meanwhile, Major Bulk,
head of the state troopers, acting on a tip that one
of the Pruitt children had appendicitis, arranged
for a dog team to be sent by plane from Laconia,

New Hampshire, and also dispatched a squad of troopers to attempt a crossing of the bay. Snow began falling at sundown, and during the night three of the rescuers lost their lives about half a mile from shore, trying to jump from one ice cake to another.

The plane carrying the sled dogs was over southern New England when ice began forming on its wings. As the pilot circled for a forced landing, a large meat bone which one of the dogs had brought along got wedged in the socket of the main control stick, and the plane went into a steep dive and crashed against the side of a powerhouse, instantly killing the pilot and all the dogs, and fatally injuring Walter Ringstead, 7, of 3452 Garden View Avenue, Stamford, Conn.

Shortly before midnight, the news of the appendicitis reached the Pruitt house itself, when a chartered autogiro from Hearst's International News Service made a landing in the storm and reporters informed Mr. Pruitt that his oldest boy, Charles, was ill and would have to be taken to Baltimore for an emergency operation. Mrs. Pruitt remonstrated, but Charles said his side did hurt a little, and it ended by his leaving in the giro. Twenty minutes later another plane came in, bearing a surgeon, two trained nurses, and a man from the National Broadcasting Company, and the second Pruitt boy, Chester, underwent an exclusive appendectomy in the kitchen of the Pruitt home, over the Blue Network. This lad died, later, from eating dried apricots too soon after his illness, but Charles, the other boy, recovered after a long convalescence and returned to the island in the first warm days of spring.

He found things much changed. The house was gone, having caught fire on the third and last night of the rescue when a flare dropped by one of the departing planes lodged in a bucket of trash on the piazza. After the fire, Mr. Pruitt had apparently moved his family into the emergency shed which the radio announcers had thrown up, and there they had dwelt under rather difficult conditions until the night the entire family was wiped out by drinking a ten-per-cent solution of carbolic acid which the surgeon had left behind and which Pa Pruitt had mistaken for grain alcohol.

Barnetuck Bay seemed a different place to Charles. After giving his kin decent burial, he left the island of his nativity and went to dwell on the mainland.

The Supremacy of Uruguay

Fifteen years after the peace had been made at Versailles, Uruguay came into possession of a very fine military secret. It was an invention, in effect so simple, in construction so cheap, that there was not the slightest doubt that it would enable Uruguay to subdue any or all of the other nations of the earth. Naturally the two or three statesmen who knew about it saw visions of aggrandizement; and although there was nothing in history to indicate that a large country was any happier than a small one, they were very anxious to get going.

The inventor of the device was a Montevideo hotel clerk named Martín Casablanca. He had got the idea for the thing during the 1933 mayoralty campaign in New York City, where he was attending a hotel men's convention. One November evening, shortly before election, he was wandering in the Broadway district and came upon a street rally. A platform had been erected on the marquee of one of the theatres, and in an interval between

speeches a cold young man in an overcoat was singing into a microphone. "Thanks," he crooned, "for
all the lovely dee-light I found in your embrace . . ." The inflection of the love words was
that of a murmurous voice, but the volume of the
amplified sound was enormous; it carried for
blocks, deep into the ranks of the electorate. The
Uruguayan paused. He was not unfamiliar with
the delight of a love embrace, but in his experience
it had been pitched lower—more intimate, concentrated. This sprawling, public sound had a curious
effect on him. "And thanks for unforgettable
nights I never can replace . . ." People swayed
against him. In the so bright corner in the too
crowded press of bodies, the dominant and searching booming of the love singer struck sharp into
him and he became for a few seconds, as he later
realized, a loony man. The faces, the mask-faces,
the chill air, the advertising lights, the steam rising
from the jumbo cup of A. & P. Coffee high over
Forty-seventh Street, these added to his enchant-
ment and his unbalance. At any rate, when he left
and walked away from Times Square and the great
slimy sounds of the love embrace, this was the
thought that was in his head:

If it unhinged me to hear such a soft croon-
ing sound slightly amplified, what might it not
do to me to hear a far greater sound greatlier am-
plified?

Mr. Casablanca stopped. "Good Christ!" he
whispered to himself; and his own whisper frightened him, as though it, too, had been amplified.

Chucking his convention, he sailed for Uruguay
the following afternoon. Ten months later he had
perfected and turned over to his government a
war machine unique in military history—a radio-
controlled plane carrying an electric phonograph
with a retractable streamlined horn. Casablanca
had got hold of Uruguay's loudest tenor, and had
recorded the bar of music he had heard in Times
Square. "Thanks," screamed the tenor, "for unforgettable nights I never can replace . . ." Casablanca prepared to step it up a hundred and fifty
thousand times, and grooved the record so it would
repeat the phrase endlessly. His theory was that a
squadron of pilotless planes scattering this unen-
durable sound over foreign territories would immediately reduce the populace to insanity. Then
Uruguay, at her leisure, could send in her armies,

subdue the idiots, and annex the land. It was a most engaging prospect.

The world at this time was drifting rapidly into a nationalistic phase. The incredible cancers of the World War had been forgotten, armaments were being rebuilt, hate and fear sat in every citadel. The Geneva gesture had been prolonged, but only by dint of removing the seat of disarmament to a walled city on a neutral island and quartering the delegates in the waiting destroyers of their respective countries. The Congress of the United States had appropriated another hundred million dollars for her naval program; Germany had expelled the Jews and recast the steel of her helmets in a firmer mold; and the world was re-living the 1914 prologue. Uruguay waited till she thought the moment was at hand, and then struck. Over the slumbrous hemispheres by night sped swift gleaming planes, and there fell upon all the world, except Uruguay, a sound the equal of which had never been heard on land or sea.

The effect was as Casablanca had predicted. In forty-eight hours the peoples were hopelessly mad, ravaged by an ineradicable noise, ears shattered,

minds unseated. No defence had been possible
because the minute anyone came within range of
the sound, he lost his sanity and, being daft, proved
ineffectual in a military way. After the planes had
passed over, life went on much as before, except
that it was more secure, sanity being gone. No one
could hear anything except the noise in his own
head. At the actual moment when people had been
smitten with the noise, there had been, of course,
some rather amusing incidents. A lady in West
Philadelphia happened to be talking to her
butcher on the phone. "Thanks," she had just said,
"for taking back that tough steak yesterday. And
thanks," she added, as the plane passed over, "for
unforgettable nights I never can replace." Lino-
type operators in composing-rooms chopped off in
the middle of sentences, like the one who was set-
ting a story about an admiral in San Pedro:

I am tremendously grateful to all the ladies of San
Pedro for the wonderful hospitality they have shown the
men of the fleet during our recent maneuvers and thanks
for unforgettable nights I never can replace and thanks
for unforgettable nights I nev-

To all appearances Uruguay's conquest of the
earth was complete. There remained, of course,

the formal occupation by her armed forces. That her troops, being in possession of all their faculties, could establish her supremacy among idiots, she never for a moment doubted. She assumed that with nothing but lunacy to combat, the occupation would be mildly stimulating and enjoyable. She supposed her crazy foes would do a few rather funny, picturesque things with their battleships and their tanks, and then surrender. What she failed to anticipate was that her foes, being mad, had no intention of making war at all. The occupation proved bloodless and singularly unimpressive. A detachment of her troops landed in New York, for example, and took up quarters in the RKO Building, which was fairly empty at the time; and they were no more conspicuous around town than the Knights of Pythias. One of her battleships steamed for England, and the commanding officer grew so enraged when no hostile ship came out to engage him that he sent a wireless (which of course nobody in England heard): "Come on out, you yellow-bellied rats!"

It was the same story everywhere. Uruguay's supremacy was never challenged by her silly subjects, and she was very little noticed. Territorially her

conquest was magnificent; politically it was a
fiasco. The peoples of the world paid slight attention to the Uruguayans, and the Uruguayans, for
their part, were bored by many of their territo-
rials—in particular by the Lithuanians, whom they
couldn't stand. Everywhere crazy people lived
happily as children, in their heads the old refrain:
"And thanks for unforgettable nights . . ." Bil-
lions dwelt contentedly in a fool's paradise. The
earth was bountiful and there was peace and
plenty. Uruguay gazed at her vast domain and saw
the whole incident lacked authenticity.

It wasn't till years later, when the descendants of
some early American idiots grew up and regained
their senses, that there was a wholesale return of
sanity to the world, land and sea forces were restored to fighting strength, and the avenging struggle was begun which eventually involved all the
races of the earth, crushed Uruguay, and destroyed mankind without a trace.

The Man Who Changed in Appearance

WHEN HE JOINED THE RANKS OF THE WELL-TO-DO, Mr. Ungadine failed to reap the enjoyment of his improved station in life because he decided he was being followed. The notion hit him one day when he was coming out of his bank after making a deposit of $275 and saw a man with a turned-up collar step from a doorway and swing in behind him. After that, almost everywhere he went, he was shadowed. He began to recognize familiar faces among the persons in his rear, and at night he could hardly sleep for thinking of his sneaky spies. There was the one in the painter's uniform; there was the small, beady one with jerky movements (a dope, thought Mr. Ungadine); and there was the tall, well-built, suave one, neatly turned out, with the pearl-gray hat snapped down all around. These men, Mr. Ungadine was sure, met at the end of the day, compared notes, talked him over. He was certain that every movement he made was known to the mob.

Too timid to report the matter to the police,
Mr. Ungadine resorted to disguising his appearance, to make the task of following him more
difficult. At first he merely took pains never to
wear the same overcoat two days running. But he
was still followed. He took to buying hats and ro-
tating them like crops; one day it would be the
snap brim, the next day it would be the rolled
brim, the next day the beret. He let his hair grow
unusually long, then suddenly had it cut unusually
short. He affected extremes of pace when walking.
He smoked sometimes a pipe, sometimes a cigarette, sometimes a cigar—so that on Monday, say,
you would have an Ungadine in a brown raglan,
brown snap-brim hat, walking slow, smoking a
pipe; on Tuesday you would have a wholly different Ungadine—derby, chesterfield coat, cigarette,
cane, brisk step.

Mrs. Ungadine noticed the great variety and
activity in her husband's accoutrement and manner. On the whole she was rather pleased—he
seemed toned up, and she believed him happy.
But one day, when he showed up with the ends of
his mustache waxed, a cape flung across his shoulders, a patch over one eye, and a marmoset riding

on his arm, she had to look twice before she could be sure it was he. Poor Ungadine—this was only the beginning of the domestic confusion which was to end in sorrow. Next day the mustache was gone, the patch had become a pair of smoked glasses, and he strode to work in a second lieutenant's uniform and a Benda mask. It was not many evenings later that he was arrested, in his own home, on the complaint of his own wife, who believed herself victimized by an utter stranger. Ungadine, appearing in court in slacks and a turtle-neck sweater and carrying ski poles, pled guilty to unlawful entry and assault, and was sentenced to serve a term in jail. When last I heard of him, he was still in prison, but had become a trusty in the carpenter shop and had made himself a uniform with vertical instead of horizontal stripes and patch pockets, which he wore on alternate days. Mrs. Ungadine remarried after seven years, under the Enoch Arden law.

Irtnog

ALONG ABOUT 1920 IT BECAME APPARENT THAT more things were being written than people had time to read. That is to say, even if a man spent his entire time reading stories, articles, and news, as they appeared in books, magazines, and pamphlets, he fell behind. This was no fault of the reading public; on the contrary, readers made a real effort to keep pace with writers, and utilized every spare moment during their waking hours. They read while shaving in the morning and while waiting for trains and while riding on trains. There came to be a kind of tacit agreement among members of the reading public that when one person laid down the baton, someone else must pick it up; and so when a customer entered a barber shop, the barber would lay aside the *Evening Globe* and the customer would pick up *Judge*; or when a customer appeared in a shoe-shining parlor, the bootblack would put away the *Racing Form* and the customer would open his briefcase and pull out "The Sheik." So there was always somebody reading something. Motormen of trolley cars read while they waited on the switch. Errand boys read while walking from the corner of Thirty-ninth and Madison to the corner of Twenty-fifth and Broadway. Subway riders read constantly, even when they were in a crushed, upright position in which nobody could read his own paper but everyone could look over the next man's shoulder. People passing newsstands would pause for a second to read headlines. Men in the back seats of limousines, northbound on Lafayette Street in the evening, switched on tiny dome lights and read the *Wall Street Journal*. Women in semi-detached houses joined circulating libraries and read Vachel Lindsay while the baby was taking his nap.

There was a tremendous volume of stuff that had to be read. Writing began to give off all sorts of by-products. Readers not only had to read the original works of a writer, but they also had to scan what the critics said, and they had to read the advertisements reprinting the favorable criticisms, and they had to read the book chat giving some rather odd piece of information about the writer— such as that he could write only when he had a ginger snap in his mouth. It all took time. Writers gained steadily, and readers lost.

Then along came the *Reader's Digest*. That was

a wonderful idea. It digested everything that was being written in leading magazines, and put new hope in the hearts of readers. Here, everybody thought, was the answer to the problem. Readers, badly discouraged by the rate they had been losing ground, took courage and set out once more to keep abreast of everything that was being written in the world. For a while they seemed to hold their own. But soon other digests and short cuts appeared, like *Time*, and "The Best Short Stories of 1927," and the new Five Foot Shelf, and Wells' "Outline of History," and *News-Week*, and *Fiction Parade*. By 1939 there were one hundred and seventy-three digests, or short cuts, in America, and even if a man read nothing but digested or selected material, and read continuously, he couldn't keep up. It was obvious that something more concentrated than digests would have to come along to take up the slack.

It did. Someone conceived the idea of digesting the digests. He brought out a little publication called *Pith*, no bigger than your thumb. It was a digest of *Reader's Digest, Time, Concise Spicy Tales*, and the daily News Summary of the *Herald Tribune*. Everything was so extremely condensed

that a reader could absorb everything that was
being published in the world in about forty-five
minutes. It was a tremendous financial success, and
of course other publications sprang up, aping it:
one called *Core*, another called *Nub*, and a third
called *Nutshell*. *Nutshell* folded up, because, an
expert said, the name was too long; but half a
dozen others sprang up to take its place, and for
another short period readers enjoyed a breathing
spell and managed to stay abreast of writers. In
fact, at one juncture, soon after the appearance of
Nub, some person of unsound business tendencies
felt that the digest rage had been carried too far
and that there would be room in the magazine field
for a counter-digest—a publication devoted to restoring literary bulk. He raised some money and
issued a huge thing called *Amplifo*, undigesting
the digests. In the second issue the name had been
changed to *Regurgitans*. The third issue never
reached the stands. *Pith* and *Core* continued to
gain, and became so extraordinarily profitable that
hundreds of other digests of digests came into
being. Again readers felt themselves slipping. *Dis-
tillate* came along, a super-digest which condensed
a Hemingway novel to the single word "Bang!"

and reduced a long *Scribner's* article about the
problem of the unruly child to the two words "Hit
him."

You would think that with such drastic conden-
sation going on, the situation would have resolved
itself and that an adjustment would have been set
up between writer and reader. Unfortunately,
writers still forged ahead. Digests and super-
digests, because of their rich returns, became as
numerous as the things digested. It was not until
1960, when a Stevens Tech graduate named Abe
Shapiro stepped in with an immensely ingenious
formula, that a permanent balance was established
between writers and readers. Shapiro was a sort of
Einstein. He had read prodigiously; and as he
thought back over all the things that he had ever
read, he became convinced that it would be possible to express them in mathematical quintes-
sence. He was positive that he could take everything that was written and published each day, and
reduce it to a six-letter word. He worked out a
secret formula and began posting daily bulletins,
telling his result. Everything that had been written
during the first day of his formula came down to
the word "Irtnog." The second day, everything
reduced to "Efsitz." People accepted these mathe-

matical distillations; and strangely enough, or perhaps not strangely at all, people were thoroughly
satisfied—which would lead one to believe that
what readers really craved was not so much the
contents of books, magazines, and papers as the
assurance that they were not missing anything.
Shapiro found that his bulletin board was inade-
quate, so he made a deal with a printer and issued
a handbill at five o'clock every afternoon, giving
the Word of the Day. It caught hold instantly.

The effect on the populace was salutary. Readers, once they felt confident that they had one-
hundred-per-cent coverage, were able to discard
the unnatural habit of focussing their eyes on
words every instant. Freed of the exhausting consequences of their hopeless race against writers,
they found their health returning, along with a
certain tranquillity and a more poised way of
living. There was a marked decrease in stomach
ulcers, which, doctors said, had been the result of
allowing the eye to jump nervously from one
newspaper headline to another after a heavy meal.
With the dwindling of reading, writing fell off.
Forests, which had been plundered for newsprint,
grew tall again; droughts were unheard of; and
people dwelt in slow comfort, in a green world.

The Crack of Doom

SEVERAL MONTHS PRIOR TO THE END OF THE WORLD, the elms died off. The blight which killed them was introduced into this country with a shipment of elm logs consigned to a novelty hat concern, which manufactured funny hats for men's banquets. Within a few weeks, so persistent was the fungus, there was not an elm tree left in the East. The loss, particularly in New England, was regarded as unfortunate but not significant; and the E. I. du Pont de Nemours Company soon brought out a superior funny hat made out of a new substance called Fibrotex. The willows went shortly after.

In almost all parts of the world people began to notice a great increase in rainfall. Boston experienced a precipitation of five inches within twenty-four hours, followed by a long period of drought. Meteorologists, unable to predict the weather with any accuracy, took to writing about it at great length for the papers. It was apparent to everyone that tropical storms were occurring more frequently than in any period of time within memory. These disturbances were of great violence; they moved farther to the northward and westward than observers had ever noticed before, and in consequence interfered with the plans of a larger number of people.

Coincidental with these atmospheric disturbances was a series of alarming economic disturbances, arising from the increasing irrelevancy of industrial life. The motor-paced bicycle race was characteristic of the inverted activity of the period. The heath hen disappeared, and in isolated sections of the world sleeping sickness broke out. During one of the worst of the storms which ravaged the New Jersey coast, one of the encephalitis victims was offered a large sum if he would allow himself to be exhibited at the Century of Progress Exposition.

Science was making rapid strides. Its findings were of a brilliant rather than a comforting nature, most of them merely demonstrating the futility of earlier scientific advance. In the field of medicine, for example, it was discovered that the gold inlays commonly used by dentists in filling teeth were being gradually absorbed into people's bloodstreams, causing varicose veins. Tularemia, once thought to be the result of the bite of a rabbit, was found to be the result of the widespread use of iodine on cuts and abrasions. A new disease, which began to attack the backs of people's necks in middle life, was traced to the custom (which had come in around 1910) of feeding orange juice to very young babies; doctors found that persons who had been fed orange juice when tiny experienced a stiffening of the muscles of the neck before sixty, making it hard for them to turn around and look behind them. In agriculture, through the use of metallic sprays, fruits and vegetables were brought to a new high point of perfection: an apple was produced as large as a pumpkin, its only disillusioning quality being that it contained enough arsenic residue to kill whoever might eat it.

Radio, even before the elms died, was reaching extraordinary heights. The sounds emitted by studios seeped into houses and even into automobiles. A preponderance of programs advertised products which were "soft" and "smooth," or which made, or tended to make, life itself "soft" and "smooth." Manufacturers of beauty cream said it would make the face softer and smoother. Manufacturers of motor oil said the oil would make one's motor run softly, with greater smoothness. Manufacturers of baking powder said the powder would produce cake of a new, softer, smoother texture. This softness and smoothness of all things in the radio field, coupled with various automatic devices such as self-opening doors and self-running furnaces, contributed only slightly to human happiness, because although many things were softer and smoother, the average person didn't feel well enough to enjoy them.

In the midst of these disturbing manifestations, a research was being conducted by a young man named Elias Gott, in a Norfolk jacket. Mr. Gott was following up the tenable and sombre theory that the increase in the number of storms, blights, and floods was caused by radio waves. He had rigged up an observatory in his garage and had proved to his own satisfaction that periods of excessive radio advertising of soft, smooth articles were followed by violent storms, and that the size of the storm area was in direct proportion to the duration of the program and the softness of the product. It was also his belief that the vast increase in broadcasting was causing the earth to deviate from its path around the sun.

In order to complete the experiments by which

he hoped to prove this theory, it was necessary for
him to make a balloon flight into the stratosphere,
carrying delicate instruments. The event awak-
ened national interest; the take-off, near a dead
elm on the outskirts of Batavia, N. Y., was attended
by reporters, photographers, and radio announcers
in chartered planes. Mr. Gott did not delay. He
rose straight and high, quickly outdistancing the
planes of the announcers, and disappeared out of
sight. When he returned a couple of hours later,
he carried with him positive proof that radio waves
were causing the earth to veer from its orbit, and
that instead of following an elliptical course it
wasn't following any particular path at all.

In landing, Gott broke his arm and had to be
taken to the Batavia Memorial Hospital; but this
minor accident only served to increase the activity
of the radio people. NBC dispatched six radio-
equipped Curtiss Condors from the Floyd Bennett
Airport to Batavia with instructions to dive in
formation at the windows of the hospital and give
the radio audience a first-hand account of Gott's
condition.

"We're going to pick up messages from these
planes," said the voice at the studio, "and alternate

them with the reports coming through from the bedside, in order to give you the complete details of the wonderful achievement that went on there this afternoon. This is Ted Garnett speaking. Can Robert Tersh hear me? Calling Robert Tersh, piloting the Curtiss Condor Number One from Floyd Bennett Field. If you can hear me, Bob, I wish you would cut in and give the members of the radio audience a little picture of how things look up there in the darkness over the hospital where . . . [Another voice] Tersh speaking, Tersh speaking, here we are in the Number One Condor, we've got six thousand feet under us, and there they are!—the lights of Batavia, twinkling down there in the blackness where Elias Gott, the gamest little flier who ever lived, is lying with a broken arm after his magnificent stratosphere hop . . . [The studio] That was Robert Tersh in the Condor giving you a direct flash from the scene of the Gott flight itself. Wait a minute, now, here's a flash from the bedside, I'll let you have Mike Melcher, who is in the corridor right outside Gott's door. All right, pick it up, Mike. . . . [Another voice] This is Melcher in the Batavia Memorial Hospital, we've set up shop here right outside

Gott's door and have just sent in a note reading
'A million congratulations on the magnificent job
you did in the cause of scientific achievement' and
have received an answer back in Gott's characteristic cryptic style: 'Many thanks for your note, it
ought not be long now.' Incidentally, his arm
is . . . [The studio] This is Graham McNamee
at the studio, we're trying our darndest to pick up
Bob Tersh, who is leading the Condors from Floyd
Bennett Field; wait a minute, have you got Tersh,
Harry? All right, pick it up, Bob! [Voice from the
plane] Tersh talking, Tersh talking, we've just
completed a series of power dives from three thousand feet at the hospital window, and I want to say
before I go any further that this is some night, clear
and bright, and every star doing its stuff; and folks,
a little note of tragedy has crept into this flight—
the last plane of the squadron piloted by Eddie
Geer has been reported out. We've just picked up
a message from a private operator saying that the
plane crashed in thick fog near Elmira. Eddie was
killed instantly and I want to say that a gamer little
flier never lived . . . [Studio] McNamee speaking, thanks Bob! We've just had a check on Eddie
Geer's magnificent and tragic end in the dense fog

near Elmira, and believe me you never saw a sorrier lot of boys than we here at this end of the line. We just picked up the flash a minute ago and already we have sent out two more Condors from the field which are winging their way through the dark this very second to Elmira to the scene of the crash in order to give you first-hand information of the tragic and heroic crackup of Eddie Geer. I'm going to give you back to Mike Melcher now, at the Batavia Hospital, who will tell you how Gott is."

It was during this broadcast that Elias Gott's theory about the effects of radio waves on the earth's orbit turned out to be correct. The earth, already far off its course, swung wide and loose into the firmament, hit a fixed star, and went up in brilliant flame. The light was noticed on Mars, where it brought a moment of pleasure to young lovers; for on Mars it is the custom to kiss one's beloved when a star falls.

II. Easy Essays on Hard Subjects

Dusk in Fierce Pajamas

R AVAGED BY PINK EYE, I LAY FOR A WEEK SCARCE caring whether I lived or died. Only Wamba, my toothless old black nurse, bothered to bring me food and quinine. Then one day my strength began to return, and with it came Wamba to my bedside with a copy of *Harper's Bazaar* and a copy of *Vogue*. "Ah brought you couple magazines," she said proudly, her red gums clashing.

In the days that followed (happy days of renewed vigor and reawakened interest), I studied the magazines and lived, in their pages, the gracious lives of the characters in the ever-moving drama of society and fashion. In them I found surcease from the world's ugliness, from disarray, from all unattractive things. Through them I escaped into a world in which there was no awkwardness of gesture, no unsuitability of line, no people of no importance. It was an enriching experience. I realize now that my own life is by contrast an unlovely thing, with its disease, its banalities, its uncertainties, its toil, its single-

breasted suits, and its wine from lesser years. I
am aware of a life all around me of graciousness
and beauty, in which every moment is a tiny pearl
of good taste, and in which every acquaintance
has the common decency to possess a good back-
ground.

Lying here in these fierce pajamas, I dream of
the *Harper's Bazaar* world, the *Vogue* life; dream
of being a part of it. In fancy I am in Mrs. Cecil
Baker's pine-panelled drawing-room. It is dusk.
(It is almost always dusk in the fashion magazines.) I have on a Gantner & Mattern knit jersey
bathing suit with a flat-striped bow and an all-
white buck shoe with a floppy tongue. No, that's
wrong. I am in chiffon, for it is the magic hour
after bridge. Suddenly a Chippendale mahogany
hors-d'œuvre table is brought in. In its original
old blue-and-white Spode compartments there
sparkle olives, celery, hard-boiled eggs, radishes—
evidently put there by somebody in the employ
of Mrs. Baker. Or perhaps my fancy wanders away
from the drawing-room: I am in Mrs. Baker's
dining-room, mingling unostentatiously with the
other guests, my elbows resting lightly on the dark
polished oak of the Jacobean table, my fingers

twiddling with the early Georgian silver. Or perhaps I am not at Mrs. Baker's oak table in chiffon
at all—perhaps instead I am at Mrs. Jay Gould's
teak-wood table in a hand-knitted Anny Blatt
ensemble in diluted tri-colors and an off-the-face
hat.

It is dusk. I am dining with Rose Hobart at
the Waldorf. We have lifted our champagne
glasses. "To sentiment!" I say. And the haunting
dusk is shattered by the clean glint of jewels by
Cartier.

It is dusk. I am seated on a Bruce Buttfield
pouf, for it is dusk.

Ah, magazine dreams! How dear to me now are
the four evenings in the life of Mrs. Allan Ryan,
Junior. I have studied them one by one, and
I feel that I know them. They are perfect little
crystals of being—static, precious. There is the
evening when she stands, motionless, in a magnificent sable cape, her left arm hanging grace-
fully at her side. She is ready to go out to dinner.
What will this, her first of four evenings, bring
of romance, or even of food? Then there is the
evening when she just sits on the edge of a settee
from the Modernage Galleries, the hard bright

gleam of gold lamé topping a slim, straight, almost
Empire skirt. I see her there (the smoke from a
cigarette rising), sitting, sitting, waiting. Or the
third evening—the evening with books. Mrs. Ryan
is in chiffon; the books are in morocco. Or the
fourth evening, standing with her dachshund, herself in profile, the dog in full face.

So I live the lives of other people in my fancy:
the life of the daughter of Lord Curzon of Kedles-
ton, who has been visiting the Harold Talbotts
on Long Island. All I know of her is that she
appeared one night at dinner, her beauty set off by
the lustre of artificial satin and the watery fire
of aquamarine. It is all I know, yet it is enough;
for it is her one perfect moment in time and space,
and I know about it, and it is mine.

It is dusk. I am with Owen Johnson over his
chafing dish. It is dusk. I am with Prince Matcha-
belli over his vodka. Or I am with the Countess de
Forceville over her bridge tables. She and I have
just pushed the tables against the wall and taken
a big bite of gaspacho. Or I am with the Marquis
de Polignac over his Pommery.

How barren my actual life seems, when fancy
fails me, here with Wamba over my quinine.

Why am I not to be found at dusk, slicing black bread very thin, as William Powell does, to toast it and sprinkle it with salt? Why does not twilight find me (as it finds Mrs. Chester Burden) covering a table with salmon-pink linens on which I place only white objects, even to a white salt shaker? Why don't I learn to simplify my entertaining, like the young pinch-penny in *Vogue*, who has all his friends in before the theatre and simply gives them champagne cocktails, caviar, and one hot dish, then takes them to the show? Why do I never give parties after the opera, as Mr. Paul Cravath does, at which I have the prettiest women in New York? Come to think of it, why don't the prettiest women in New York ever come down to my place, other than that pretty little Mrs. Fazaenzi, whom Wamba won't let in? Why haven't I a butler named Fish, who makes a cocktail of three parts gin to one part lime juice, honey, vermouth, and apricot brandy in equal portions—a cocktail so delicious that people like Mrs. Harrison Williams and Mrs. Goodhue Livingston seek him out to get the formula? And if I *did* have a butler named Fish, wouldn't I kid the pants off him?

All over the world it is dusk! It is dusk at Armando's on East Fifty-fifth Street. Armando has taken up his accordion; he is dreaming over the keys. A girl comes in, attracted by the accordion, which she mistakes for Cecil Beaton's camera. She is in stiff green satin, and over it she wears a silver fox cape which she can pull around her shoulders later in the evening if she gets feeling like pulling a cape around her shoulders. It is dusk on the Harold Castles' ranch in Hawaii. I have risen early to shoot a goat, which is the smart thing to do in Hawaii. And now I am walking silently through hedges of gardenias, past the flaming ginger flowers, for I have just shot a goat. I have on nothing but red sandals and a Martex bath towel. It is dusk in the Laurentians. I am in ski togs. I feel warm and safe, knowing that the most dangerous pitfall for skiers is *color*, knowing that although a touch of brilliance against the snow is effective, too much of it is the sure sign of the amateur. It is the magic hour before cocktails. I am in the modern penthouse of Monsieur Charles de Beistegui. The staircase is entirely of cement, spreading at the hemline and trimmed with padded satin tubing caught at the neck with a bar of milk chocolate. It is dusk in Chicago. I am standing beside Mrs. Howard Linn, formerly Consuelo Vanderbilt, formerly Sophie M. Gay, formerly Ellen Glendinning, formerly Saks-Fifth Avenue. It is dusk! A pheasant has Julian Street down and is pouring a magnificent old red Burgundy down his neck. Dreams, I'm afraid. It is really dusk in my own apartment. I am down on my knees in front of an airbound radiator, trying to fix it by sticking pins in the vent. Dusk in these fierce pajamas. Kneeling here, I can't help wondering where Nancy Yuille is, in her blue wool pants and reefer and her bright red mittens. For it is dusk. I said *dusk*, Wamba! Bring the quinine!

How to Tell a Major Poet from a Minor Poet

AMONG THE THOUSANDS OF LETTERS WHICH I RE-
ceived two years ago from people thanking me for
my article "How to Drive the New Ford" were several containing the request that I "tell them how
to distinguish a major poet from a minor poet." It
is for these people that I have prepared the following article, knowing that only through one's ability
to distinguish a major poet from a minor poet may
one hope to improve one's appreciation of, or con-
tempt for, poetry itself.

Take the first ten poets that come into your
head—the list might run something like this:
Robert Frost, Arthur Guiterman, Edgar Lee Masters, Dorothy Parker, Douglas Fairbanks, Jr.,
Stephen Vincent Benét, Edwin Arlington Robin-
son, Lorraine Fay, Berton Braley, Edna St. Vincent
Millay. Can you tell, quickly and easily, which are
major and which minor? Or suppose you were a
hostess and a poet were to arrive unexpectedly at
your party—could you introduce him properly:

"This is Mr. Lutbeck, the major poet," or "This is Mr. Schenk, the minor poet"? More likely you would have to say merely: "This is Mr. Masefield, the poet"—an embarrassing situation for both poet and hostess alike.

All poetry falls into two classes: serious verse and light verse. Serious verse is verse written by a major poet; light verse is verse written by a minor poet. To distinguish the one from the other, one must have a sensitive ear and a lively imagination. Broadly speaking, a major poet may be told from a minor poet in two ways: (1) by the character of the verse, (2) by the character of the the poet. (Note: it is not always advisable to go into the character of the poet.)

As to the verse itself, let me state a few elementary rules. Any poem starting with "And when" is a serious poem written by a major poet. To illustrate—here are the first two lines of a serious poem easily distinguished by the "And when":

And when, in earth's forgotten moment, I
Unbound the cord to which the soul was bound . . .

Any poem, on the other hand, ending with "And

how" comes under the head of light verse, written by a minor poet. Following are the *last* two lines of a "light" poem, instantly identifiable by the terminal phrase:

> Placing his lips against her brow
> He kissed her eyelids shut. And how.

All poems of the latter type are what I call "light by degrees"—that is, they bear evidences of having once been serious, but the last line has been altered. The above couplet, for example, was unquestionably part of a serious poem which the poet wrote in 1916 while at Dartmouth, and originally ended:

> Placing his lips against her brow
> He kissed her eyelids shut enow.

It took fourteen years of knocking around the world before he saw how the last line could be revised to make the poem suitable for publication.

While the subject-matter of a poem does not always enable the reader to classify it, he can often pick up a strong clue. Suppose, for instance, you were to run across a poem beginning:

> When I went down to the corner grocer
> He asked would I like a bottle of Welch's grape juice
> And I said, "No, Sir."

You will know that it is a minor poem because it deals with a trademarked product. If the poem continues in this vein:

"Then how would you like a package of Jello,
A can of Del Monte peaches, some Grape Nuts,
And a box of Rinso—
Or don't you thin' so?"

you may be reasonably sure not only that the verse is "light" verse but that the poet has established some good contacts and is getting along nicely.

And now we come to the use of the word "rue" as a noun. All poems containing the word "rue" as a noun are serious. This word, rhyming as it does with "you," "true," "parvenu," "emu," "cock-a-doodle-doo," and thousands of other words, and occupying as it does a distinguished place among nouns whose meaning is just a shade unclear to most people—this word, I say, is the sort without which a major poet could not struggle along. It is the hallmark of serious verse. No minor poet dares use it, because his very minority carries with it the obligation to be a little more explicit. There are times when he would like to use "rue," as, for instance, when he is composing a poem in the A. E. Housman manner:

When drums were heard in Pelham,
    The soldier's eyes were blue,
But I came back through Scarsdale,
    And oh the . . .

Here the poet would like to get in the word
"rue" because it has the right sound, but he doesn't
dare.

So much for the character of the verse. Here are
a few general rules about the poets themselves. All
poets who, when reading from their own works,
experience a choked feeling, are major. For that
matter, all poets who read from their own works
are major, whether they choke or not. All women
poets, dead or alive, who smoke cigars are major.
All poets who have sold a sonnet for one hundred
and twenty-five dollars to a magazine with a paid
circulation of four hundred thousand are major.
A sonnet is composed of fourteen lines; thus the
payment in this case is eight dollars and ninety-
three cents a line, which constitutes a poet's ma-
jority. (It also indicates that the editor has probably been swept off his feet.)

All poets whose work appears in "The Conning
Tower" of the *World* are minor, because the
World is printed on uncoated stock—which is of-

fensive to major poets. All poets named Edna St. Vincent Millay are major.

All poets who submit their manuscripts through an agent are major. These manuscripts are instantly recognized as serious verse. They come enclosed in a manila folder accompanied by a letter from the agent: "Dear Mr. ——: Here is a new group of Miss McGroin's poems, called 'Seven Poems.' We think they are the most important she has done yet, and hope you will like them as much as we do." Such letters make it a comparatively simple matter for an editor to distinguish between serious and light verse, because of the word "important."

Incidentally, letters from poets who submit their work directly to a publication without the help of an agent are less indicative but are longer. Usually they are intimate, breezy affairs, that begin by referring to some previously rejected poem that the editor has forgotten about. They begin: "Dear Mr. ——: Thanks so much for your friendly note. I have read over 'Invulnerable' and I think I see your point, although in line 8 the word 'hernia' is, I insist, the only word to quite express the mood. At any rate, here are two new offerings. 'Thrush-

Bound' and 'The Hill,' both of which are rather timely. I suppose you know that Vivien and I have rented the most amusing wee house near the outskirts of Sharon—it used to be a well-house and the well still takes up most of the living-room. We are as poor as church mice but Vivien says, etc., etc."

A poet who, in a roomful of people, is noticeably keeping at a little distance and "seeing into" things is a major poet. This poet commonly writes in unrhymed six-foot and seven-foot verse, beginning something like this:

When, once, finding myself alone in a gathering of
    people,
I stood, a little apart, and through the endless confusion
    of voices . . .

This is a major poem and you needn't give it a second thought.

There are many more ways of telling a major poet from a minor poet, but I think I have covered the principal ones. The truth is, it is fairly easy to tell the two types apart; it is only when one sets about trying to decide whether what they write is any good or not that the thing really becomes complicated.

Fin de Saison—Palm Beach

SPECIAL TO ALMOST ANY METROPOLITAN DAILY

PALM BEACH, FLA., MARCH 31.—THE MARRIAGE of Nancy Ann Bloodgood, daughter of Mr. and Mrs. Willis Fernandez Peel of Point Watchout, who have been spending the month as guests of the Parker Travises in their ocean-front villa, will take place in St. Thomas's on Labor Day, 1936, it was announced here today by Mrs. Trask Trap, sister of Mrs. Peel and formerly Lady Crenshaw Foote, who was divorced from Viscount Sanper Toogood in February, 1923, and has spent recent years in Paris and traveling with her stepson, Sir Horace Elsinore, Bart., F.T.B., L.L.U., C.C.C., P.W.A., a charter member of the Automobile Club of Rangoon. The church will be decorated with white chameleons and pink oleanders and the following will be bridesmaids: Nancy Van Der Weird, Nancy Fenner, Nancy Prankly, Nancy Toogood Wenn, Nancy DeLoncy Bloodgood Toogood, sister of the groom and first wife of young "Sandy" Elsinore,

Nancy Fenner, and Lady Spurt Melton, sister of the bride's stepfather and known as a true dog lover. Mr. Fordyce is a student at Lawrenceville.

Mrs. James T. Afterguard entertained 1,425 friends at a luncheon in the patio of the Breaker Arms today. They discussed Lilyan Tashman's funeral.

Arrivals at Salle d'Armes Vince-on-Sea include Serge Aspirin and Madame Aspirinskaya, and Lord and Lady Herman Schulte, Lady Schulte being the daughter of Trelawney Alden and descended from a band of Seminole Indians on her mother's side. "The Indians started out on my father's side and changed over later after they got to know Dad," Lady Schulte likes to tell friends.

Rioting broke out in the cabaña of El Mintz last night when agitators representing the beach-umbrella hoisters overturned Mrs. Prudence Stickles and put a brick through her windshield.

John Peter Baggs, little son of Viscount and Slipshod Baggs, gave a sandcrab party for 123 little playmates in the basement of Bradley's yesterday. They played sand crab and won. Prizes went to Lloyd Demarest, Allan Nuts, and Percy Guam Stotzberry, 7, 8, and 9 respectively.

The temperature of the water was 72, air 73, at the Municipal Pier this morning. Rails and oils were off one to three points in sympathy with the beach-umbrella interests.

At the dog races the other night one of the dogs bit the following: Mrs. H. Fenner Euling, of Louisville, Ky., who wore a yellow and orange chiffon with velvet girdle and dropped shoulder line; Lady Polinor Sibitzky, of East Orange, in a crêpe frock of dusty pink with a wide girdle of rhinestones and oyster-shells; Baron Temple Irksome, first son of Earl and Mother Dunruly, Castle Dunruly on the Llangollenen-Dunruly in County Limerick, Blasket Blasket. The Baron's town house is at 10 Downing Street and he is a member of the exclusive Turf and Surf Club. The dog was sent away for examination but the veterinary reported that there was nothing much the matter with him. The Baron was given the Schick test.

The private railway car of Henry C. Rappleyea, maker of Chocolate Frenzies, was removed from the lawn opposite the Royal Poinciana Tuesday by nomads. Four people from West Palm Beach were injured in the disorders which followed.

Molton de Corbignac, former spermweight

champion of the world, is seen daily at the cabaña of Aimee Tendril (Fritzi Ferguson).

Post-season pastimes and diversions of the winter colony include chewing the living bark off royal palms, caponizing mourning doves, and racing verbenas. The high neck is returning for beach wear, and one sees a great deal of fustian in large checks, often with a double row of silk fringe tied at the front where it is most needed.

A lady from the lower middle classes had the misfortune to be stung by a Portuguese Man o' War while in bathing this morning off the foot of Australian Avenue. She suffered severe pain in both "legs." The Florida press maintained a dignified silence.

Princess and Mr. Ludhvigk Dhavidh Pankhg gave a dinner dance at their villa, Casa Spray, last night for Strangler Lewis.

The cabaña of Lady Woolworth-Hollingwurth-Scheslinger has been condemned as a firetrap.

The Allsinger Kipps have left for Bar Harbor with a small party of friends on the Kippses' ice yacht Thermidor for the smelting. Many amusing parties have been scheduled during their stay "down east," and while there they will dare each other to hold their tongues against the cold runners.

Loch Ness is closed for the season.

The Rimpools have closed their villa and taken an umbrella on the Municipal Beach.

Your correspondent, who is down here in connection with a CWA project for diverting the effluvia of the proletariat from Lake Worth, feels better already. But the lake still smells at twilight.

Small Thanks to You

A LITTLE WHILE AGO IN A MAGAZINE I READ AN ITEM about the Music Hall usher who awoke the sleeping patron by nudging him and saying, "Thank you, sir!" It happens that I have been making a study of abnormal politeness in America, and therefore am keen to hear about cases such as the above. Perhaps you, in turn, would be interested in some of my findings in this field.

The use of "Thank you" by the doer of a favor, instead of by the recipient, is met with fairly frequently in this country. I have named it the Reverse Acknowledgment. In the Reverse Acknowledgment the thankee becomes the thankor, for no reason which anybody has been able to put his finger on. Waiters in restaurants frequently use the Reverse Acknowledgment: you ask a waiter to bring you a pack of cigarettes and he replies, "Thank you!" or sometimes, "Thank you sommach!" Here thankee not only becomes thankor but he further complicates the affair by forgetting to bring the cigarettes. This variant I call the Reverse Acknowledgment with Subsequent Coma. More and more I eat at home.

Closely related to the Reverse Acknowledgment is what I have termed the Idiot Please, or Petition After Statement of Fact. You encounter this most frequently in elevators. The elevator operator stops at the twelfth floor and, in a fit of inspired nonsense, calls out, "Twelve, please!" as though the very act of arriving there required the indulgence of the people in the car. Luckily the Idiot Please is pretty well confined to lifts, and has not worked its way into general conversation. If the practice of using "Please" after every statement of fact were to gain universal acceptance, you can imagine the consequences. A simple conversation between mother and son would sound something like this:

"Hello, Ma, I'm home from school, please."

"Hello, son, I see you are, please."

"I got sixty in spelling today, please, Ma."

"That's nothing, son. I tripped and fell down the back stairs, please."

Such a conversation would have a polite, but not an intelligent, sound.

There is still another type of abnormal politeness which I have run across from time to time. I refer to what I call, for lack of a better name, the Promotional Apology, or Abject Puff. Business concerns and institutions are masters of the Abject Puff. I recall going into the New Yorker Hotel one time and picking up a printed card which said "Please forgive our west wall. We are preparing it for a new and interesting decorative scheme by Witold Gordon. We hope soon to unveil it and ask for your indulgence in the meantime." I can still remember how foolish it made me feel to have this large, able-bodied hotel saying "Forgive my west wall," like a twittery young housewife apologizing for the looks of her living room.

Another case of the Abject Puff was when the Cunard Line posted a notice in their Fifth Avenue window: "Sorry, but this window is not large enough to hold the new 22-foot model of the new superliner Queen Mary." They were so ashamed of this structural shortcoming, they have hardly mentioned the Queen Mary since.

I have a great many other examples of abnormal politeness, and also considerable data on certain allied phenomena in the field of extreme American cuteness and institutional ecstasy. But I won't trouble you further, except to mention that a man in Pittsburgh once got his laundry back and with it was a slip which said:

THIS WORK HAS BEEN IRONED BY
Dolores with pleasure

The man is still living in Pittsburgh, and believes that the American fantasy reached its peak with this unheard-of girl's experience: the hot laundress at her steaming board, ironing the unknown customer's shirt with loving care, starching the bosom with pleasure.

Well, little reader, goodbye, please.

As the Oith Toins

[AFTER READING A NOVEL BY GLADYS HASTY
CARROLL]

I WAS SAYING TO MRS. JANOWSKI THE OTHER EVE-
ning that spring will soon be here. She had just
come in from Gristede's, her strong round arms
full of pâté, and as she entered the warm apartment
where the lamps scattered the early dusk, there
came with her the first good smell of coal gas that
told us both that the janitor was damping the furnace. The warm weather would soon be upon us.

"Yes," she said, "soon we will be able to put the
ivy plant out on the fire escape on rainy days."

Mrs. Janowski went over to the shelf and began
moving among her preserves, stacking up piles of
oranges and corn flakes, and taking down a can of
soup. She went easily about her task, and when
one of the children ran to her, begging for something to eat, she opened up a box of crackers with
competent, sure strokes of the knife. As I watched
her, so capable, so calm, it seemed incredible that
it would soon be spring again.

How solemnly, I thought, the days follow one another in soft succession. The Dog Show is over. Hockey players still flash across the brown ice at the Garden, but they, too, will be gone before long. To-day I heard a barrel organ, and I know that some evening as I come out of my office and start down the Avenue toward the spot where I take the bus I shall meet a cart full of pink geraniums.

Life is good, here in the apartment with Mrs. Janowski and the children. It is pleasant to wake before daylight on these late winter mornings and hear the town's heavy breathing, the whistles from the river, and the steady sure progress of a cross-town car. At six o'clock the milkman comes into the downstairs hall, knocking his bottles about and banging doors. In the gathering light I stare at the walls and at Mrs. Janowski's freshly washed gloves hanging on the shade-cord where she put them before she went to bed. Soon Minnie, our little terrier, comes to the door—a polite but determined black visitor in the dawn, saying Ooof, very softly, very patiently, and adding softly Mmmm. One of us, rousing with agonizing effort, goes to the door and admits her, installing her on the bed by the window, where the sun will presently strike through, to her infinite comfort and peace. Thus the tranquil morns: the lovely light filling the room and traveling round the walls, the rustle and flutter of the chintz curtains at the open south window, Mrs. Janowski's long hair like a little grove round her calm face, and the terrier surveying the garden and needing very much to be taken out into it by me.

When the spring comes we shall read in the *Times* about the first robin, and we shall go to the circus and see Clyde Beatty. They will be busy days for Mrs. Janowski, all through the morning-glory planting and the arranging of the four strings from the window-box to the top of the shutter. The children will roller-skate again and go out into the park without their leggings. In May the fleet will come in, and we shall remember suddenly that it is time to renew our driving license.

So the days pass. I can see them, live them, as I sit here now; feel the gentle push of the steadily advancing year. I see cherries ripening in the push-carts; under my bare feet are the hot sands of the Long Island beaches in early July on those first aching Sundays, and the sun-tan oil rubbed with sand into the blistered thigh; the singing pavement of the Queensborough Bridge, and the hot, tortuous return to the apartment, where slip covers make the chairs look blue because the slip covers are blue. Ice will tinkle in Mrs. Janowski's glass as she comes out of the kitchenette with its rows of freshly bought green olives shining in the light, and on her calm, capable brow will stand small beads of perspiration. "It's almost time," she will say, "to begin to think about who will take care of the fish while we are away on vacation."

Then there will be pleasant Sundays when we shun the beaches and stay quietly in town, motionless, scarcely breathing—days when the heat sprawls untidily over the island like a Sunday paper. People will leave their shades up, and I shall be able to sit dreaming at the open window at evening, watching the young portrait painter take her bath in the tiny studio apartment across the way. Night and day the threnodial buzz of electric fans will be in our ears. Toward the end of summer a few spears of timothy grass will usurp the morning-glory box and a caterpillar will appear from nowhere. The morning-glories will wither, and it will be the grasses' day. They will stand there, plumed and proud, waving their seed-pods in the warm breeze. On clear evenings when the heat is less intense, the city will swim in a lovely bath of light, and a lone member of the Salmagundi Club will venture out to sit for a few moments on the little balcony overlooking the Avenue. In September the mosquitoes will come; and one fine morning the superintendent of the building will appear at our door, wrench in hand, and we shall watch solemnly while he removes the stove and hides it in the trunk room, in readiness for the visit of the building inspector.

I see it all so clearly: the bright tragedy of the yellow fall, the day we drive out to the Danbury Fair, our car laden with applejack, to lean on the rail watching the trotting races. And after the Fair the Rodeo, and after the Rodeo Halloween. I see the town in October, with calendulas in the flower shops and pumpkins on the stands. I will bring home a pumpkin for a jack o' lantern; and three days later Mrs. Janowski will have a time trying to wedge it onto the dumb-waiter with the rest of the garbage. And then, before we know it, Christmas

Eve, and the search on the uppermost closet shelf for the tree ornaments.

Christmas Eve! It will be five years for us in the apartment, come Christmas. I was just saying to Mrs. Janowski, five years is a long time to have lived in one apartment.

Ex-Uncle

(BY THE AUTHOR OF "EX-WIFE," "EX-HUSBAND,"
AND "EX-MISTRESS")

All the names, places, and dates in this narrative have been changed beyond possible recognition. The circumstances have been altered beyond the possibility of identification.

I WAS BORN IN 1893, THE UNWANTED THIRD SON OF a librarian. Both my parents were sick. Outside my window was a rabbit hutch. All day I heard rabbits sitting. I knew then that if I ever had a niece she would have sinus trouble. There was that in me.

The doe rabbit was a little bit of all right. Whatever else my childhood was or wasn't, it had carrots. The rabbit ate them backwards, beginning at the core and gnawing out. At the age of three I went to live in a carbarn in the outskirts of Detroit, and from there moved to a small unlighted apartment in Forty-eighth Street near Lexington Avenue. The rabbits had eczema. I used to put salve on them, rubbing it into their fur and into the small skull-socket behind their great silky ears. I was a sensitive child, always put on my pajamas before taking off my pants. That kind of boy.

The August following my coming to New York was hot. The sun was reflected from the pavement into the unlighted apartment, and smelled crisp and flat, like a curtain seam. September dragged into October, October dragged into November, November dragged into December, and when Union Square was deep under a fall of snow I met my niece. Her name was Minnie Feeley. That is, that is what people in the reference-room of the library called her. Her real name was Marion Feeley. I showed her the rabbits, and we laughed together as only uncle and niece can laugh in a great city. There is a small broken place in the pavement in Fortieth Street just south of the library. We were both fond of the spot and used to go there noons and talk about sinus trouble. In after years, when the rabbits had eaten all the carrots, I never passed that place without thinking of Minnie.

The April after I started seeing Minnie, I knew that something was going to happen. I knew that I was going to have tonsilitis. How could I tell Minnie? Yet I knew that I must. My father was be-

ginning to notice my condition and would soon
turn me out of the apartment. I wanted Minnie—
wanted, oh so much, to sit with her in Fortieth
Street as we used to do, but I was afraid to see her
and tell her. Finally one day I followed her home,
and as she was turning in at the door, I just blurted
it out. I remember Taft was president.

The following September I realized that matters could be put off no longer. I had a friend who
worked for a doctor. He told me about the Tonsil
and Adenoids Hospital, where they accepted unmarried men who were going to have tonsilitis. I
fainted in the taxi going there. The driver's name
was Angelo Pattulo. In the admitting office of the
hospital they gave me bicarbonate of soda. I said
my name was Julius Womrath. The first question
they asked me was whether I had a niece. I decided
not to lie.

"Yes."

"Where does she live?"

"In England."

"Has she parents?"

"They are dead."

"Where did they die?"

"In England."

Coming out of the ether I heard mandolins. The mandolins had eczema, so I took salve and rubbed it into their strings, rubbing it well down between the tuning pins. I was terribly weak, and too exhausted to think. It was good to be in bed. I invented a cock-and-bull story to tell my father. I had the hospital authorities tell him I was dead. Lying there in the ward I thought of the rabbits and of the outskirts of Detroit.

When I got out of the hospital I took a small unheated room near the Williamsburg Bridge. Every morning the landlady brought me caramels and a copy of the Mirror. I didn't want to take a bath. My throat was healing and one day, seeing a longshoreman moving boxes around, I stretched my neck and moved my arms and knew that my body belonged to myself again.

I didn't see Minnie until the fall of 1923. I remember it was an early fall, and the autumn colors were lovely. Minnie was with a man named Trimble.

"You know," she said to me quietly, "you were really an awful ass."

I smiled back at her.

A Guide to the Pronunciation of Words in "Time"

IT IS ONE THING TO READ *Time*; IT IS ANOTHER TO pronounce the words correctly. All of us recognize, for example, in reading the weekly news-magazine, that the word *cinemaddict* is a happy marriage of the word *cinema* with the word *addict*, and that the word presumably means "one who frequents the movies"; but to date there has been no serious study of such word formations with a view to establishing the pronunciation—on the wild chance that some day the words might be uttered out loud. *NewYorker*worthy is this attempt of mine to suggest a handy table of reference by which such remarkable words may become part of the living, spoken tongue, instead of just dumb.

Unlike that of most persons, much of my reading is done aloud. Even when I read silently, I move my lips and form every syllable; thus my need to know how a word sounds is a very real one. Prior to the Roosevelt administration it did not occur to me to explore the phonetics of *Time-*

language, but when, one day, I stumbled on the expression "RFChairman Jones," I knew that I would either have to work out a practical sound pattern for such elisions or cancel my subscription, which still had a year and five months to run. One's first impulse in pronouncing such an adherent noun as *RFChairman* is to treat it as one does the name Mdivani—simply not sound what I call the "impossible capitals." The word then becomes just *Chairman*. This is obviously incomplete and unsatisfactory; the word loses its definitive quality. One next tries supplying the missing punctuation marks, and the noun becomes *R. F. Chairman*. But this, too, is unsatisfactory and confusing. Shorn of the *C* in *R.F.C.*, the expression is politically meaningless, probably politically unwise, and looks almost like a proper name, as though one were reading about a man named R. F. Chairman Jones (his full name, we'll say, is Robert Fairfax Chairman Jones). Such a pronunciation is untenable. One then resorts to pronouncing the word as nearly as possible to the way it looks, which is accomplished by puckering the lips, screwing the mouth round and round, and lingering over the impossible capitals so that they ac-

quire an extra weight, which tends to break up the
pharyngeal clot. The result is something like this:
Rrr-uff-chair'-man Jones. This I have found to
be at once the most difficult and the most satisfying
way. It is, I am bold enough to state, the correct
pronunciation of the word. The same rule holds
for all similar bureaucratic *Time*nouns. Sometimes it becomes necessary to aspirate the prelimi-
nary capitals. Thus, *WPAdministrator Williams* is
correctly pronounced *Wwh-hu'-pad-min"is-tra-tor
Williams.*

Now let us look at the word *cinemaddict.* Here
we have two words joined together and made one.
The difficulty is the dropped *a,* which, although
better for you than a fried *a,* is none too easy on a
weak stomach. To the inquiring mind, the question immediately arises, which *a* is gone—the final
a of *cinema,* or the initial *a* of *addict*? The question
is well taken. Without answering it, one can't make
an intelligent attempt to place the accent and pronounce the word. If one believes, as many Eastern-
ers do, that the *a* was taken from *cinema,* then one
should accent the penult, and the word is *sin-i-mad'
dict,* stressed like the word *mathematics.* If, however, one believes that the *a* was taken from *addict,*

then the pronunciation obviously is *sin' i-mad-dict"*. (Note: Some *Time*unworthy readers have highhandedly changed the final *t* to *k*, cut the word up again into two parts, and simply say *cinema dick*.) I hold that none of these pronunciations is correct. It is my belief that the *a* in *cinemaddict* rightly belongs neither to *cinema* nor to *addict*, but that it is a highly concentrated, bastard vowel in which both original *a's* are concealed, along with two or three other *a's* that climbed aboard in the night. The key to pronouncing *cinemaddict* is in knowing how to prolong and extend the *a* sound until its rightful quantity is restored, which can be accomplished only by bleating. Open the mouth and say *sin-i-maa-aaaa' dict*.

A friend of ours, now thirty-seven years old, who took to stuttering at the age of thirty-five attributes his speech defect to the word *AAAdministrator*. But although it was a *Time*word that brought on his trouble, it was, strangely enough, another *Time*word that eventually was the means of curing him. Poor, stuttering, redfaced Earl Lawley got trapped in the middle of *cinemaudience* one day and couldn't get out. Held fast by the syllable *mau*, which he kept murmuring over and over, he was a pitiable sight. Many a trapped animal has had to do just what courageous, stuttering, redfaced Earl Lawley did: he calmly gnawed off the tip of his tongue and wriggled free.

Once the above general principles of pronunciation are grasped, the other queer words in *Time* fall into types and can be worked out. Often it is merely a question of where the word properly divides up. *Realmleader,* for instance, is pronounced *rē"al-mlēd'er*. *Newshawk* is *noosh-awk'*. *Newsworthy* is *new-swûr'thy,* or *swar'thy*. There are a few purely arbitrary rules which one must memorize. *Radiorator,* I have found, is best when simplified still further, and made *radiator,* or *chumley*. *Cinemactress,* instead of requiring the middle bleat, as in *cinemaddict,* is pronounced by leaving the *a* with *cinema,* restoring and transposing the vanished *a* in *actress,* and giving the primary accent to the last syllable. Thus, *sin"i-ma-ca-tress'*. The word *up* used as a verb becomes *oop,* as, "he ooped sales."

A Century of Progress

Two or three people have sent me postcards from the Fair, so I know the buildings are colored; and my sister, who lives in Chicago, tells me what a nuisance the thing is, drawing house guests as old fruit draws flies. But in the main I owe my knowledge of A Century of Progress to my nephew, an observant, keyed-up boy of thirteen, dedicated to the ideal of scientific advance. He visited the Exhibition a year ago, in company with some classmates, and has been telling me about it from time to time ever since. With a sure sense of detail, he has succeeded where others have failed: it is from him that I have learned what progress can mean. You see there was a Negro who would take his eye like this and while you were looking he would pop it out of its socket. There wouldn't be any skin around it. That was in a big place called the Odditorium where there was a square thing in the centre, I mean a table with glass over it for the oddities, the things that weren't alive, and booths all around. One fellow was marooned on an island

and the natives all had their breasts pierced. He had his pierced and he would put a bar through them and lift weights with it. He was a big strong guy and you could tell he had holes through them.

The old order changeth. Old things fade; new methods, new ideals come. My nephew has made me love the world as it is today. There was a man who had lost his larynx from an operation and he figured out a way to speak by belching. And there were some swell things in the medical exhibit: a model of a man lying on a table being operated on to have his leg cut off. His leg was in a bucket of blood. And photographs of people with leprosy and sleeping sickness and George Washington's false teeth.

A lady would sit in a sort of a little truck like an express wagon (Onward!) and a man would fasten the string to his eyelid and pull it across the floor with his eyelid. It was good. There was a man who could write on pieces of rice, he would write the Lord's Prayer on a grain of rice. And a fellow had a machine and he'd have a light up here, so you'd hold your hand against a screen and he'd turn a crank and then you'd move your hand away and the shadow would stay there, then slowly fade away. And a baby with three legs.

I think it was in the Hall of Science that there
was a model showing you how to brush your teeth.

The sweep of the century carries me along with
it. My nephew hopes to revisit the Fair, look up
the man who was ossified, stiff as a bone, with his
legs crossed. He had a trained nurse and the nurse
would pull his leg up and down (laughter) and his
whole body would go with it. He was ossified. (In
the Transportation Building a toy cannon, shooting balls at unbreakable glass, and the glass not
breaking.) And the skull of a man who had a crowbar blown through his head. He lived for years but
then he died and this was his skull.

And I know the buildings are colored.

Eeny Meeny Miny Mo

CATCH BARBARA FOLTZ, LISTED IN THE SOCIAL REGISTER, BY THE TOE

HAVE YOU EVER TRIED TO DECIDE WHICH OF ARTHUR Murray's dance instructors you would like to dance with, from reading about them and looking at their pictures in the *Herald Tribune*? I have! Have you ever weighed Grace Hazelton against Barbara Foltz? Have you ever pitted Florence Leighton Smith's beauty against Gladys Pell's patience? I do all the time.

And where do I get? Where, to be sure, does Arthur Murray get? I am one of the best prospects for a dance studio in New York City—I am as good material as any dance studio could hope for: clumsy, awkward, diffident, no social charm, no sense of rhythm, no tuxedo. I am the perfect customer for a dance studio; as my friends put it I am "made to order for Arthur Murray." Yet what comes of it all? I look at the likenesses of his six dance instructors, I memorize the descriptions of their traits and capabilities, and I simply can't make up my mind which one I want, to the exclusion of the other five. I want them all. I want Barbara, Gladys, Elizabeth, Florence, Grace, Dorothy—I want to hold all six of them close to me, and make the same mistakes with every one. How can I choose one girl from that lovely galaxy, even though I crave the definite air of distinction, the subtle sophistication, the youthful vivacity which would characterize my dancing were I to register at Murray's?

Usually, as I glance at the advertisement, I start by favoring Gladys Pell, who is described as "lovely, patient, sympathetic." Those are sterling qualities. Patience is absolutely essential in my case, patience plus a kind of animal passion which makes dancing with me bearable even after it is clearly torture. Yes, patience is important; I have a bagful of tricks that would try the patience of even a Gladys Pell, not the least of which is the way I toss my head to the music and break into a little wan smile as I glide about the floor. Miss Pell is also described as "a descendant of the Pell to whom Pelham was given by King George." What an asset in a dance partner! Think how it would

break the ice for me to start talking familiarly of
Pelham, and go right on in a natural manner to
Pelham Manor, Pelham Heights, and Pelham
Wood—all the time dancing, or trying to! Nor am
I a man who stops at Pelham, either; the first thing
you know Miss Pell and I would be talking freely
about New Rochelle.

No sooner do I decide that Gladys Pell is the
instructor for me than I start reading about Elizabeth Anderson, "whose delightful manner with be-
ginners is remembered long after the pupil becomes an excellent dancer." Not a word about her
patience, mind you, but what of it? What if she
hasn't got the patience of a Pell? Patience be
damned, what I want is memories. I want a girl I
can remember. Yes, remember long after. Ten
years after, if you want to know. Twenty years,
twenty-five, twenty-six, twenty-seven years. I don't
want to go to Arthur Murray's studio, put my arm
around a sweet girl, and then go away and never
think of her again. I'm no cad, or "rotter."

But here! Look at this! Look at Florence Leighton Smith, of New York City and Miami, who is
"a graduate of Smith College, class of 1929. Miss
Smith's pupils at Arthur Murray's quickly acquire

that confidence and poise so essential to good dancing." After all, that's what I'm after, isn't it? Or
isn't it? No matter how patient a girl is with me,
no matter how long I remember a girl after dancing with her, what do those things get me if I still
have no poise? Even to have no poise in the presence of, or in the arms of, a Smith graduate, would
be something. I don't say it would be everything,
but I say it would be something. Yes, sir, Florence
is my girl.

Florence is my girl nothing! Dorothy Lucille
Calvo is my girl. "Dorothy Lucille Calvo, of Sa-
vannah, Georgia, where she was socially promi-
nent. Her charming personality is expressed in her
dancing and reflected in the dancing of Arthur
Murray's pupils." That's what's been the matter
with my dancing—it didn't have anything of the
Old South in it, none of the languor, none of the
charming stupefaction, none of the hatred of the
North with its damned Bluecoats. Ah wants a
dayncin' pahtnah lak' Missy Do'thy; Ah wants t'lay
mah hayd against the soft Suth'n cheek of a gal
from ole G'ogia. Then Ah can daynce! Mmm-
mmm, Ah, can sutinly daynce!

Well, there you are. I get all steamed up over

Dorothy, Florence, Elizabeth, Gladys, only to trans-
fer my allegiance the next moment to Grace Hazelton, under whose talented tutelage society people
and businessmen alike find it a pleasure to keep
their dancing young. Grace has her little day, and
I find myself belonging lock, stock, and barrel to
Barbara Foltz, whose family is "listed in the Social
Register." Under the "F"s, probably.

It's no use. I'll never be able to narrow my choice
down to one dance instructor. I think what I better
do is have all the girls down to my place some afternoon for cocktails. No, not you, Mr. Murray—just
the girls and me. Any time after five-thirty.
Dancing.

Hark! Hark! The Turncoats

[AN OPEN LETTER TO THE ASSOCIATION OF NATIONAL
ADVERTISERS]

Gentlemen:

THIS MORNING'S PAPER SAYS YOU ARE GETTING BE-
hind a nationwide campaign to abolish fear. If that
is the case, you are a bunch of old turncoats. Who
started the idea of American fear, anyway, if it
wasn't you? Who frightened me into thinking I
had bad breath? Who scared me into supposing I
was intestinally sick, almost dead? Who made me
feel socially inferior? Who roused in me the fear
that I was perspiring at a dance? Who kept telling
me my flat silver wasn't of the correct design, and
that my automobile would skid into another car at
any minute, and that my throat was being burned
by smoking the wrong brand of cigarettes, and that
my gums were receding into my poor, thick head?
Gentlemen, I am asking!

It has taken you years to build up in me my
fears; you mustn't flatter yourselves that you can

break them down overnight—my fears aren't so easily abolished, they are made of sterner stuff. I am not just a tiny bit frightened, I am scared stiff. So you see you have made your bed, and now you'll have to lie in it, gentlemen. And if you roll and toss all night long, that's all right with me.

It is part of your plan, I see by the paper, to restore "normal spending habits." Gentlemen, I am laughing. You have no notion of what my normal spending habits are, and what's more I don't believe you want to know. If you knew, it would scare you. You don't want to restore *my* normal spending habits, you want to restore *your* conception of my normal spending habits. In other words, you want to abolish my fears temporarily, until you can get round to selling me another mother-of-pearl garbage can for my kitchen. Well, my hearties, I'm scared and I'm staying scared!

Strangely enough, gentlemen, in the pleasant rigor of the past two or three years, I have had an opportunity to orient myself to what are called hard times, and to examine the standards of living to which people have been subjected by reason of their financial inability to respond to certain kinds of advertising. I have found a stimulus in this new and solemn condition, and I have had a little time for quiet thinking because instead of being out buying something every minute I was home indulging in the more monastic pleasures of the nonpurchaser. Gentlemen, it was great. In this state of tranquillity, too, I formed friendships with some of the most thoroughly frightened consumers in America—people who had been reduced, through the golden age of buying, to a condition of sanitary misery, or shall I say dismal elegance? These people (some of the nicest folks in the world, at heart) feel exactly the way I do about abolishing fear: they are perfectly willing to have it abolished, but they don't want any advertising men doing it. They feel you aren't the type.

Gentlemen, this has turned into quite a long letter, but I regard you as the daddies of American timidity, and I thought I had better warn you not to try to abolish any fears of mine. I know, from reading your stuff, just how unfortunate, dumb, bleak, and sick I am. My spirit, gentlemen, is broken.

Getting Along with Women

WHO IS THIS WONDER MAN IN *Harpers Magazine*, this prince of good fellows who gets along with women? Did any of you read that article? I mean the article called "Getting Along with Women," written by a man who shows right off the bat what women think of him by signing the piece "Anonymous." He gets along so well with women he dassent even sign his name. Well, *I* dast. My name is White, and I *don't* get along with women. I would rather be at continual odds with women, and am.

One thing that struck me right away about Anonymous's article was that he apparently has no real taste for women anyway, and of course it's easy enough to get along with women if you don't care for them. It simply isn't a problem. Anonymous says some very fine things about women, but they don't ring true. They haven't got what I call "glow." According to Anonymous, women don't even belong to the same race as men. He says that what you've got to have to get along is the ability to "see in every woman something of the woman eternal." Well, that's just what I can't do. I see in every woman the woman temporary, or the woman dishevelled, or the woman terribly attractive, or the woman beloved. The reason I can't see the woman eternal is that I don't think woman is a day more eternal than I am.

Another thing he says about women is that they are the "keepers of the life-tides." I think that is silly, too. I've never seen a woman with a life-tide, and if a woman did have a life-tide, she probably couldn't keep it, because if she's anything like my Gloria, she can't keep anything. I can just see Gloria trying to keep a life-tide when she doesn't even know where she put the key to the front door except she thinks it was in her purse. It is as keeper of the life-tides, according to Old Know-it-all, that woman has a truly great kinship with Nature, far greater than man's. "Once let a man understand this relationship between woman and Nature, and he will bow before her outbursts and condone them." Oh, is that so? Well, sir, I have found out that when a woman has burst out at me, it wasn't because of any kinship with Nature, it was usually because I damn well had it coming to me. Furthermore, if anybody around my house is going to have kinship with Nature, *I'll* handle it. That's understood. I am just as "natural" as any woman, and I'm far naturaller than a lot. I know enough about Nature not to call her Mother, for one thing. I call her Father. Old Father Nature. Good old Pop! I have been out messing around with old Pop Nature when a lot of my fine women friends were safe indoors with their lares, penates, bridge lamps, and old copies of *Harpers*. No, woman isn't the keeper of any tides. Woman is, on the whole, scared to death of tides, particularly the strong tides which characterize the eastern section of the coast of Maine around Mount Desert Island.

But I'll let that go. Let's see how a man should behave to get along with women, according to old Daddy Anonymous, the king of Get Alongers.

"If you really are intent on getting along well with your woman," he says, "anything you do to help things along is justifiable." Now isn't that just fine? For the sake of getting along, anything goes. Anonymous, even if I were intent on getting along with my (as you call her) woman, I could think of a dozen things which I would not consider justifiable. And so could she. In fact, she could probably

think of more things than I could, which is another
reason we don't get along—she's always got the edge
on me, that way. You want to know some of the
things I would not consider justifiable? Lying is
one. Acting different from the way I feel is two.
Giving in by so much as an inch in a matter of
principle is three. Offering her a handkerchief is
four. And if you want the other eight, you know
my name.

"Keep your head," says Anonymous, "and you'll
be able to manage her all right." Manage her, eh?
That gives you a pretty good idea of what the
author of "Getting Along with Women" means by
getting along with women. He means managing
women. He is talking not about marital harmony
or sexual rapport or general amicability, he is talking about managerial prowess. I am not quibbling
here, or turning a chance phrase to my advantage:
Anonymous mentions "managing" over and over
again. In the very first paragraph he introduces a
poor, inept male who couldn't get along with
women. "The man," he says, "has not managed
her." And again: "Most women can be managed
with praise." Manage, manage, manage. The picture I got of Anonymous's woman, after reading

his article, was of a little girl whom he kept out in the kitchen and fed on Ken-L Ration. Once in a while he gave her a couple of life-tides to play with, and some praise to keep her from screaming and annoying the neighbors, and all the time he kept murmuring to himself what a wonderful creature she was (for him to manage), and seeing in her "something of the woman eternal," a kin of Nature, warmly human, wanting to be possessed and "enwrapped in the strong mantle of maleness." Not just wrapped, mind you, but *en*wrapped. But does he ever go out there and enwrap her? Not that I can make out.

I just don't understand this man. He says men are imaginative, women are realistic. "For confirmation of this truism," he says, "I give you Hans Christian Andersen, the Brothers Grimm, Andrew Lang, Homer, Virgil, and the nameless spinner of Scheherazade's adventures." O.K., Anonymous, two can play at gift-giving. I give you Marie de France, the Sisters Brontë, Beatrix Potter, Selma Lagerlöf, Lady Murasaki, Laura E. Richards, Helen Bannerman, Lily F. Wesselhoeft, and Beatrice Lillie. No, on second thought I think I'll *keep* Beatrice Lillie. You don't deserve her, and I doubt if you could manage her.

This fellow Anonymous not only claims to know all about women, he seems to know all about us men, too. All about me, I don't doubt. Listen to this one: "One chief reason for the failure of a man in love to get along with his woman seems to him of course to be a tendency on her part to ask too much. . . . He grows resentful, they quarrel, and then what? He turns to some other woman for comfort." I do, eh? All right, Smarty, what's the other woman's name? Come on, what's her name? You're pretty sure of yourself, aren't you? I bet you'd be surprised to know what I *do* turn to, when I grow resentful and quarrel. It's not another woman either. It's a pineapple maraschino nut sundae with a whiskey base. Ha!

He seems to know all about my carnal side, too. He speaks of certain men (and I can only assume he means me) who "think of women primarily as bodies sent for man's gratification. . . . Given a pretty woman and a drink, and they become clumsily chivalrous." Well, Sir Galahad, it might interest you to learn that given a pretty woman and a drink, I do *not* become clumsily chivalrous, I become grace itself. I have friends who keep the finest liquors and the prettiest women always on hand, just so they can give them to me and see how beau-

tifully I carry on. How d'ya like that, Anonymous?
And whether I think of a woman as "primarily" or
"secondarily" a body sent for man's gratification is
quite possibly a point too fine for an old Get
Alonger like you to get mixed up with, you old
Amicable Relations Establisher, you. Don't start
me off about the body of woman, please, or this will
grow too esoteric for anything.

After he has explained how to get along with
women you love, Anonymous plunges on into new
fields: he explains how to get along with women
you *don't* love—as though anybody cared. For
heaven's sake, who wants to get along with a
woman in whom he's not interested? I say chuck
her and get one you *do* love, one who fascinates you
so completely that getting along with her is practically out of the question. But not Anonymous.
No, he says: "The clever man lets the same qualities in him be apparent to all women, whether
sweetheart, friend, or business associate—his maleness, his consideration, his understanding. And
toward all women alike, if he be wise, he exhibits a
genuine appreciation, just as in their various rela-
tionships he displays a sense of humor." Anonymous apparently got his idea about the necessity

of having a sense of humor from a friend of his named Charley Calder, whom he quotes. Charley says that a man "has got to be diplomatic, and he's got to have a sense of humor." I think Charley Calder is just as odd a character, in his own way, as Anonymous. Diplomacy and a sense of humor, to my mind, are mutually exclusive qualities. They do not coexist. Sense of humor is just another name for sense of directness; diplomacy means sense of indirectness, or mild chicanery. I don't see how a man can have both, or, if he had them, how he could use 'em against a woman.

But enough of this tedious theme! I will leave Anonymous to his amicability, his sense of humor, his little hypocrisies and artifices. It's five o'clock. Twilight is settling down on the city, and with it comes the infinitely alluring prospect of going forth to meet a pretty woman, and of not making the slightest effort to get along with her, and of succeeding.

Swing Low, Sweet Upswing

I HAVE BEEN ASKED TO INTERPRET THE RECENT TAIL-spin of pig iron. In a technocracy such as ours, one must go behind the facts; but in this article I not only intend to go behind the facts but I intend to stay there and never come out.

It is marvellous back here behind the facts—just like being backstage at the theatre. Walter Lippmann is here, and George Soule, and Stuart Chase, and Sir Arthur Salter, and Professor Seligman, and Howard Scott, and John Maynard Keynes; in short, all the big people of the depression. I have never seen so many economists together before, nor they me. Hundreds of facts have been piled together to form a curtain, and all of us are busy writing. It is warm here, and comfortable, and I wish I had found this place a lot sooner.

Now about pig iron. Pig iron is like anything else in this world that is unwanted. You don't want any pig iron, do you? All right, neither do I. No wonder it's in a tailspin. Now, why *don't* we want it? Simply because pig iron has no style, no class, no rugged individualism; and this is an age when the consumer demands the niceties of life and cannot be satisfied by the mere sight of a lot of pig iron. The standard of living has gone up. The Hippodrome has been sold. England has paid. Money is cheap, and for the price of a chunk of pig iron, or three freight-car loadings, one can go to the movies.

I

No one can discuss the economic situation (and how I wish that were the end of a sentence) without deciding whether he is an inflationist or a deflationist. I can see the good points of both systems and I have worked out a scheme for a planned society which takes into consideration the merits of everything. Everybody knows that there is a paradox involved here: that, for the first time in the history of the world, we are dealing with the Economics of Abundance. The Economics of Abundance means that there is an abundance of economists. In other words, the harder the times get, the harder the reading gets. It's a vicious circle. People who should be out purchasing something are sitting indoors reading an interpretative article in a magazine. (That goes for you, reader!) The more they read, the less they buy; and the less they buy, the sooner it's next month. Each new month brings a new issue of the magazine, so where is this thing going to end? Or don't you care any more?

MY PLAN

My plan has ten points, which is five more than Charles Butterworth's and four less than Woodrow Wilson's.

First. I would organize all technologists and put Raymond Duncan in charge, to teach them the hand loom. I would even go behind technologists to technologists' mothers, and put the issue of over-production squarely up to them. I knew a technologist's mother once, and I swear it would have killed the old lady if she had realized that a son of hers was to grow up to disgrace his country by improving machinery.

Second. I would alternate the periods of deflation and inflation. This is where the vicious circle comes in—comes in, that is, if I'll *let* it in. You see, the more a government or a corporation reduces its expenses the better shape it gets to be in finan-

cially but the more people also get put out of jobs
and the more people get put out of jobs the fewer
articles they can afford to purchase from the company that fired them and therefore the worse shape
instead of the better shape the company gets to be
in financially. Maybe I could make this clearer by
citing the United States Navy. I like to cite the
Navy because for a long time we haven't spoken.
Let us say, then, that for the purposes of economy
the Navy be disbanded. That would be *de*flation,
and would suit me to a T. But . . . think of all
those sailors out of a job! We economists have to
think of everything. Once off the government's
payroll, those sailors wouldn't be buying tobacco,
wouldn't be taking Riverside Drive girls to the
cinema, wouldn't be putting any money into circulation. Some of the men might even become anti-
social. Therefore, say the inflationists, the Navy
should be kept going even though it isn't paying.

My plan calls for both systems. I want certain
months of the year given over to inflation, and
certain months to deflation. Months with an "r"
in them could be months in which all corpora-
tions and governments would adopt a policy of inflation. Whoop everything up. Double people's

pay. Start the old ball rolling. Plenty of credit, plenty of beer, plenty of articles in the magazines by me. Never mind technology, hello France. Things would boom. The standard of living would go up, people would buy automobiles, stocks would soar, and good times would be here again. It would be costly, but anything really worth while in life has its price. Then along would come a month without an "r" and deflation could be ushered in. Budgets slashed, men laid off, Navy disbanded, the wheels of industry (Raymond Duncan) slowed down. It wouldn't hurt anybody because everybody would be ready for it. If Daylight Saving works, why wouldn't my plan?

Third. I would abolish second, third, and fourth-class mail. Should have been done long ago.

Fourth. I would put to work all unemployed men who want to work. I would supply them with hairpins and set them to work picking cordial-shop cards out of private letterboxes and throwing them away. A general fund could easily be raised to pay their salaries.

Fifth. I would stabilize all industries that are mutually exclusive—like nudism and garment-making. If they won't submit to stabilization, then let the devil take the hindmost.

Sixth. I would place a government tax of two cents on the use of the words "technocracy," "upswing," "downswing," "tide," "rugged," and "crisis," payable by the writer, and retroactive.

Eighth. I would supply gasoline only to those motorists who could give a reason for wanting to drive somewhere. That would eliminate much of this driving about from one point to another by persons interested solely in atrophy during mobility.

Ninth. I would ask the Telephone Company to install an idleness signal to offset the harmful psychological effect of the busy signal. Few persons whose phones are in use are in any sense of the word busy, and the sharp indication that they are busy is undermining to the average idle citizen. The idleness signal would sound something like a yawn.

Tenth. I would provide lounges behind the facts. It's nice back here but there is no place to sit down.

R. F. Tweedle D.

IN 1923, AFTER AN INTERVAL OF UNEXPLAINED GOOD
health, I married a woman of some refinement. She
had hazel eyes and absolute pitch. I had long been
a writer, and there seemed to be but one course
open to us—agriculture. If, in the ensuing pages, I
refer repeatedly to Pearl's despondency on the
farm and her jealousy of the shoats, it is because
she moves through my life like a clear stream of
running water, activating the young corn and seal-
ing the Mason jars. In the early morning, when I
take my typewriter and my lantern to the barn and
stand for a moment listening to the heavy breathing of the creatures in the stanchions and watching
the hired man rehearsing his part in the next Little
Theatre production of "Candida," there stands
Pearl, bathed in new light, opening can after can
of prepared shoat food. We buy this by the case
direct from Charles. It costs nine dollars per case of
twenty-four cans, or a little less than eighty-three

cents a hundredweight. We mix it with anchovy paste and slaked lime in the proportion of one part fresh fruit lemonade (which we bring home from the Little Theatre) to sixteen parts soy. The shoats love it, but we never give it to them: we prefer to eat it ourselves, as it saves dishwashing.

All the dishwashing at Book Farm is done by the county agent, who visits Pearl on fetid summer afternoons when the brooder stoves have gone out and she is warming the young pullets by holding her great bombazine skirt over them. Most of the time Pearl wears no skirt—just shorts and a fez. I wear orange slacks made of sailcloth, and a postman's hat. We always bathe nude in the drinking trough in the dairy, where the cold, clear water trickles in steadily like royalties from a good piece of non-fiction. There is no plumbing in our house and not the slightest advantage or convenience. I took the wainscoting down yesterday and re-hewed it along my own lines. You don't hear the word "re-hew" used much nowadays, but I always use it and so does Pearl. We got into a merry argument, after three Manhattans, as to whether the wainscoting was ready to be bred. Our neighbor, Mr. Enoch Galway, happened by and surprised us in the midst of this badinage, and probably thought we were queer ones. Country folk have a solid worth, which is as purifying as a glass of milk.

I am a state-accredited veterinary and in lambing time I sometimes go a week at a time without sleep, my eyes open as wide as teacups. Lambing, like any other farm operation, is largely a knack, and is by no means as dangerous as it used to be. I usually take along a copy of *Life* to the lambing ground—which is in the bottom lands just this side of the stadium. There is something peaceful about the miracle of birth, and what the popular magazines don't know about it the ewe does, or thinks she does. Pearl is no help in lambing, but I leave the entire docking of the shoats' tails to her, as well as the laundering of the kilts; and to both these country chores she brings a kind of pagan excitement without which this rural existence would be a mere pause between two worlds. We made a profit on the sheep this year for the first time. I sold two of the rams to a circus for an animal act, and the government bought all the wool to stuff into the dikes along the Mississippi. I do not believe in flood control, however, nor do I derive any satisfaction except a financial one from the twenty-five-thousand-dollar-a-year income which we get from certain investments left us by Pearl's uncle, who made a fortune a generation ago by the old conventional corn-wheat-grass rotation.

The cows pay well, too. We never drink the milk, because that would mean washing the pail. Instead, we make it into clabber, and then the clabber is processed and becomes rubber, which we use for tractor tires. The tractor is invaluable to us in turning over the ground for the spring planting of fodder corn for the cows. Thus does nature pursue her inexorable cycle.

The years are a green parade with banners flying. Farming has its compensations and pays dividends in health and serenity—although the first five years we were here Pearl had shingles continuously and our doctor's bill ran well over four hundred dollars a month. I can always sell words, and it is the only crop I enjoy marketing. We grade and candle our words, and store them in the root cellar. I have taught Pearl to save only the Latin roots, and feed the others to the shoats, mixed with apple cores and middlings. Neither Pearl nor I knew what middlings were when we came here in 1923, and although she handles them every day, Pearl still doesn't know. But the serene mornings, the steady push of the year, nights compounded of mystery and good talk and cider in season, and the county agent out in the kitchen with the dirty dishes, these are what make life supportable to us and fascinating to hundreds of thousands of Americans who are aware that something rather odd is happening in this country but are not sure yet quite what it is.

III. Medicine, and Other Occult Sciences

Barge Life on a Root Canal

IT IS A MONDAY AFTERNOON, IN LATE SPRING. THE monotone of life fills me with a pleasant and in-audible singing as I walk up the Avenue. Physically I buzz with a low healthy fever, like a cricket. I am on the way to my dentist's, treading the same path that I have followed so many Monday afternoons since that first snowfall.

Without thinking where I am going, or why, I turn in at the door, enter the elevator, and announce the floor.

"Five."

There is a small mirror in one corner of the elevator. During the ascent I remove my hat, face myself in the mirror. My tie is not quite right; I make it right. A lock of hair is matted down too tight; I loosen it with a poke of my finger. At the fifth floor the elevator stops, the gate opens, and I get out.

The girl who opens the door of the reception-room is short and fair-haired. She speaks with a slightly foreign inflection.

"Good afternoon."

"How do you do?" I reply. Our greeting has always been that, since the beginning. Neither of us would think of varying it. Each feels the serenity of a completely ritualistic experience. To change would be to spoil something.

I am on the davenport in the reception-room, a copy of *Life* in my lap. I turn the pages. From the next room, where the dentist is, come occasional sounds of voices. On the hat-tree in the corner hangs the hat of the patient who is inside, in the dentist's chair. Subconsciously I realize that I don't know what the man who owns the hat looks like. A few moments later he comes through the door, his appointment over with. It is true, I did not know what he looked like. But I am not surprised by his looks. He is just a man, who takes his hat and leaves the place.

There is a wait of one minute. I close my copy of *Life*. The door into the office opens again, the girl appears.

"All right now."

She holds the door for me as I go through. Ahead of me is the empty chair, with its curious trappings—pipes, pulleys, buttons. I saunter over to the chair and drop down into it as idly as I would sit down in an easy chair at home. No one is in sight. I know that the girl has followed me into the room, but I do not look around. I cross my right leg over my left, and let my head slip back into the head-rest. Just as this is completed, the dentist appears, at my right.

"How are you?" he says.

"I'm fine," I reply.

That greeting, too, has been the same, all these Monday afternoons since the beginning of our remarkable acquaintanceship. As we exchange the greeting, a hand goes around my neck from behind, and the girl, whom I do not see, passes a small bib under my chin and ties it. I open my mouth. The dentist inserts two rolls of wadding to hold my tongue out of the way, lights a small gas jet, passes an instrument over the flame, and skillfully removes a temporary filling from a certain lower tooth, exposing the root canal. Then follow ten minutes during which the dentist treats the tooth, picking up instruments, laying them down. To this I pay not the slightest attention, having fallen into a reverie induced by keeping my mouth open. There is no pain, no sensa-

tion of any kind, beyond a dull ache of the jaws at
their unnatural position, and a slight flow of saliva
into my windpipe. Ten minutes being up, the
dentist refills the tooth quickly and skillfully, removes the wadding from my mouth, a hand
reaches around, undoes the bib, and I arise from
the chair, as refreshed as though I had had a sound
nap.

"Next Monday at three," he says.

"Yes. Goodbye, Doctor." And I am gone.

Sometimes I wonder how it all started, how I
fell into this way of life. These Monday afternoons—there must have been a beginning, when
we went into a discussion of my teeth and decided
on a tooth to work with. There must have been a
first visit, when we exchanged more than a greeting. It is all so long ago I have forgotten. From
week to week nothing changes—neither my tooth,
nor my experience, nor my attitude. Only has
there been a gradual reinforcement of my routine.
Between my dentist and me there has sprung up
a deep understanding, in which mere words would
be superfluous. Not for anything in the world
would I inquire about my tooth; and presumably
he has no intention of volunteering any informa-

tion about it. If either of us were to open the subject, it would break the charming spell under which we both are now held.

As far as I know they will go on indefinitely, these Mondays. I am perfectly content to have it so. As I say, there is no pain to speak of, no inconvenience, rather a calm feeling of well-being. The periodicity of the appointments gives my life a continuity, almost a meaning; and the total expense is not great—the whole thing comes to only sixty-five dollars a month. I have got so I look forward to Monday as the one day in the week when my life is not quite purposeless. If ever we should break off, my dentist and I, or if ever the tooth should, through constant manipulation, be worn down so thin as to be of no further use for our purposes, I would feel strangely lost. Whatever happens, however, nobody nor anything can take from us the happiness we have known during this period. I suppose times must change eventually, but no matter what comes, I shall always look back on these days, in this spring of 1930, as among the happiest of my life; I shall always regard Dr. B—— with a feeling not unlike tenderness, a loyalty not untinged with affection.

A Study of the Clinical "We"

A RECENT ARTICLE ON GRAMMAR, WHICH I READ IN a magazine, has led me to the preparation of a paper on the clinical "we." The clinical "we" is a bedside form in use among practical nurses, who find, in the sound of the plural, a little of the faded romance which still attaches to life. It is also used universally by baby nurses, who think of themselves in groups of four.

Unlike the editorial "we," which is a literary device used to protect writers from the fumes of their own work, the clinical "we" is simply a spoken form, and is rarely written. A baby nurse employs the "we" in the belief that no single person could have as much special knowledge as she has, and that therefore when she speaks it must be three other people too. Thus, when I once asked a baby nurse if she wouldn't please put a hat on my son before she took him out in a sandstorm which happened to be raging at the moment, her reply was: "We never put hats on him after June first." "You and who else don't?" I remember answering. It was my first clash with the clinical "we."

Since then I have studied it, not only in baby nurses but in dentists' assistants, ward witches, and the developers of X-ray plates. It is common to all of them, but hospital nurses use it to denote the patient, not the nurse. I know of one hospital case in which the sudden use of the clinical "we," in the presence of an elderly gentleman convalescing from an operation, threw him into a paroxysm which proved a serious setback to his recovery. It was early in the morning, and a pretty little Southern nurse, coming into his room, sang out: "We didn't change our pajamas this morning, did we?"

"No, let's do it right now!" replied the aged patient somewhat bitterly. The wry joke so excited him that he had to be given a sedative, and later a talking to.

It is probably apparent from the above examples that the clinical "we" can seldom be taken lying down, but almost always provokes a rejoinder. In hospitals the "we" is merely an unattractive figure of speech in a world of strange and unattractive details, but in the home it is intolerable. To live under the same roof with a user of the "we" is a fairly good test of a man's character. During the winter of 1931 I employed twenty-two baby nurses, one after another, before I found one who could make a sentence beginning with the word "I." I used to call them "we-uns." Every morning I would go upstairs to the nursery. "Morning, Nurse," I would say, "how you feeling?"

"We are just fine, sir," would be the courteous but silly reply.

"Canst make a sentence beginning with the word 'I'?" I would ask.

"We never make sentences that-a-way, sir," she would blush. So I would fire her and get another. Finally a little Irish girl named McGheogheoghan (pronounced McVeigh) came along, and one morning I went up and asked her how she was feeling.

"I feel terrible," she answered.

That nurse is still with us, and grows, I am happy to say, more singular every day.

Rest Room No. 2

IT WILL BE A LITTLE WHILE BEFORE THE NOVOCAINE takes effect," said the nurse gently, "so if you'll just wait in here, please . . ." She opened the door of a little room.

"Did you bring a newspaper?" "No," I replied. "But I don't need one." The nurse smiled and shut the door, and I was alone in Rest Room No. 2. I sat down on the leather bed, beside the still waters.

Nurses go out of their way, I thought, to be comforting. The upshot of it is, they frighten me. Maybe that's what they really want to do, under the skin. Take the way that nurse approached me in the matter of taking a pill, before the novocaine injection. "I'm going to ask you to take this little pill," was the way she had put it. Deliberately ominous. No pill, I don't care what it's made of, deserves that amount of mystery. Why couldn't she have said, "Happy dust, kid," and winked? I still don't know what that pill was made of. It was yellow—rather pale yellow.

Discomfited, I looked around my little rest room. In addition to the leather bed, there was a porcelain bowl, a towel, an army blanket folded neatly across the foot of the bed, a dressing table on which was an imitation tortoiseshell tray, and a little blue bottle of something. Above the dressing table was a mirror, hanging slightly crooked.

My tongue was beginning to get numb. I bit it gently, to test it. Still some feeling there. Maybe I should have brought a newspaper, after all. This is pretty dull, just sitting here, biting a numb tongue.

I noticed a picture on the wall. One of those cheerful-sayings pictures. "The house by the side of the road," it was called. Where did dentists get the idea their patients wanted to read cheerful sayings? Some advertising man sold them that idea, probably. In the picture in front of me, a man in a smock was driving a band of sheep down a road. "Let me live in a house by the side of the road, Where the race of men go by." All right, let me. Any little house is better than a rest room, especially Rest Room No. 2. What was the matter with putting me in Rest Room No. 1, anyway? Wasn't I good enough? I suppose they spotted me as a

No. 2 man the minute I came in! I went back to
reading the legend under the picture ". . . Where
the race of men go by, The men who are good and
the men who are bad, As good and as bad as I."
Just because I'm going to have an impacted wisdom tooth out, I have to start wondering how
good or bad I am, is that the idea? The hell with
how bad I am: it's stamina that's going to count in
the next few minutes, not righteousness.

I debated whether to read any more. It wasn't
fun. I decided to test my jaw again, instead. I put
my hand to my mouth. It felt like an old sponge.

"Let me live in a house by the side of . . ."
Oh, shut up. Don't read any more of that hooey
about houses. I shifted uneasily on the leather bed.
My shirt felt cold under my arm; nervous perspiration. Well, what if I am a little nervous, it's an
impacted tooth, isn't it? Means cutting the jawbone. Yes, sir, the old jawbone. None of your
simple extractions! This is where they use the
chisel, the saw, and the adz. Who was it was slain
with a jawbone and an adz? Some Bible fellow.
Well, I never had much respect for any man whose
wisdom teeth weren't impacted. Sign of effemi-
nacy, normal wisdom teeth. Any softie can get

rid of a tooth where you don't have to cut the jawbone.

I wonder where Florence Nightingale went to? I'm not going to sit here all morning looking at a cheerful saying and a crooked mirror. It's a pity they wouldn't straighten that mirror. Was I born into this lovely world to sit on a leather bed and look at a crooked mirror? I'll bet the mirror in Rest Room No. 1 is straight.

I ran my tongue around my mouth. It felt like jello. Well, bring on your knife! "Let me live in a . . ." Bring on your saw! "Let me live in a house . . ." Bring on your adz! "Let me live in a house by the . . ."

The door opened. "All ready," said the nurse, softly.

The Near-Demise of Mrs. Coe

CHARACTERS

Fred Coe
Mrs. Coe
Miss Straight, a nurse
Doctor Clarke
A little old man

SCENE

A bedroom in Mrs. Coe's apartment in New York. At the bedside is a table holding a glass of water, a clinical thermometer, a telephone, and a vase of Talisman roses. Mrs. Coe is in bed, sick as a dog.

(Enter Mr. Coe.)

MR. COE—Feel any better?

MRS. COE—No.

MR. COE—Well, I'm going to call him up; we've monkeyed round long enough.

MRS. COE—Call who up?

MR. COE—That doctor.

MRS. COE—You better let Miss Straight do it. I don't know whether we ought to, anyway.

MR. COE—Why not, for Pete's sake? You're sick, aren't you? He's your doctor, isn't he?

(Mr. Coe goes out and returns a moment later with Miss Straight, who is dressed in a white uniform.)

MISS STRAIGHT—We can't call Doctor Fenway now, Mrs. Coe. This isn't the telephone hour.

MR. COE—No, and it isn't the Tasty Yeast Hour either. But I want a doctor down here, and if you don't call him up, I'm going to. He's on the case, isn't he?

MISS STRAIGHT—Well, if Mr. Coe wants to. But *I* can't do it.

MR. COE *(picking up the phone)*—Wickersham 8-3540 . . .

MISS STRAIGHT—What is your temperature now, Mrs. Coe?

MRS. COE—A hundred and nine and a half, going on a hundred and ten.

MR. COE—Wickersham 8-3540. Yes. Hello? May I speak with Doctor Fenway? Mr. Coe. Yes. What? He's at the what? At the . . . thank you. Ask him to call me when he comes in, will you please?

MISS STRAIGHT—He's at the Poultry Show, isn't he?

MR. COE—Yes. What the hell does he do at the Poultry Show?

MISS STRAIGHT—Doctor Fenway has always been interested in poultry, Mr. Coe. He's something of a fancier.

MR. COE—I can imagine. What's that other fellow's name? I'll call him.

MISS STRAIGHT—You mean Doctor Clarke?

MRS. COE (*weakly*)—You can't call Doctor Clarke, Fred. He's an abdominalist, and this pain is entirely in my throat. It would be out of his province.

MR. COE (*looking in the phonebook*)—Province my eye. Murray Hill 3-4636. You're sick, aren't you? Murray Hill 3-4636? Yes. I'd like to speak with Doctor Clarke. I'll hold it. Doctor Clarke? This is Coe. Mrs. Coe has a very high fever, and Doctor Fenway is in Madison Square Garden, so I wondered if you could come down here? Yes. Forty East Ninth Street. No, *Ninth* Street. What? It's her throat. Thank you. (*Hanging up the phone.*) He's coming down at one o'clock.

MISS STRAIGHT—That's very strange.

MR. COE—What's very strange?

MISS STRAIGHT—His coming down here. Doctor
Clarke never takes cases below Thirty-fourth
Street. Are you sure he understood the address?

MRS. COE (*faintly from under the covers*)—I feel
as though I were going to die.

MR. COE—Nonsense! Of course you're not, darling.

MISS STRAIGHT—I'm going to have my lunch, now,
Mr. Coe. If Mrs. Coe should feel uncomfortable, would you let me know?

(*She goes out. Mr. Coe sits down at the bedside
and holds Mrs. Coe's hand. He sits that way for
about half an hour, when the doorbell rings. Doctor Clarke, wearing knickerbockers, is ushered into
the room, followed by Miss Straight, who has finished her lunch, consisting of tomato bisque,
creamed chicken, riced potatoes, romaine, checker-
berry pie, and demi-tasse.*)

MISS STRAIGHT—This is Doctor Clarke.

DOCTOR CLARKE—How do you do?

MR. COE (*rising*)—She's over here, Doctor.

(*Miss Straight has gone to the bedside and is
taking the patient's pulse.*)

DOCTOR CLARKE (*rubbing his hands*)—Cold out today.

MR. COE—Her temperature has gone up over a hundred and nine.

MISS STRAIGHT (*dropping the patient's wrist*)—Mrs. Coe is dead, Doctor.

DOCTOR CLARKE (*lighting a cigarette*)—Have you an ashtray I could use?

MISS STRAIGHT—Certainly, Doctor.

(She rushes out and returns with an ashtray which she dips in alcohol and hands to the Doctor, who is now sitting over by the window.)

MISS STRAIGHT—I didn't intend that Mr. Coe should call you, Doctor, but he insisted. I hope he didn't catch you at a bad time. Mrs. Coe's infection was localized in the throat, which is Doctor Fenway's area.

MR. COE (*at the bedside*)—Speak to me, darling.

DOCTOR CLARKE—Yes, I can't very well encroach on Fenway's area. You understand that, Mr. Coe. My practice extends from the abdominal region to a point three inches below the knee. Where is Fenway, by the way?

MR. COE—Speak to me, Mary.

MISS STRAIGHT—At the Poultry Show, Doctor
Clarke.

DOCTOR CLARKE—Is he? I was there yesterday. It's
better than last year's show, particularly the
Leghorns and Wyandottes.

(The phone rings. Miss Straight answers.)

MISS STRAIGHT—Yes? Miss Friburg? Yes, everything is satisfactory. Mrs. Coe is dead.

MR. COE—She is not. Speak to me, honey.

MISS STRAIGHT—Yes, that's right, Miss Friburg.
She died at one-three. You'll inform Doctor
Fenway, won't you? You say he's on his way
down here? Oh, that's a shame. Maybe you
could catch him at the elevator. *(She hangs up
the phone.)* It was Doctor Fenway's secretary.
He is on his way down here.

MR. COE—Thanks.

*(The door of the room opens and a nice little old
man with a beard enters. He wears a long black
coat smelling of iodoform, and carries a small black
bag.)*

LITTLE OLD MAN *(going to bedside)*—I'm old Doctor Campbell, from Framingham. I used to be

Mary's doctor when she was a little girl and I heard she was ailin' so I thought I'd come down. I got in on the noon train.

MISS STRAIGHT—Mrs. Coe is dead.

LITTLE OLD MAN—Where does it hurt?

MISS STRAIGHT—It was a throat infection.

MR. COE—Her throat hurts.

(The little old man puts on his glasses, opens Mrs. Coe's mouth with a teaspoon, peers curiously in, and extracts, after a moment, a large chicken bone.)

LITTLE OLD MAN—My, my, that must have hurt.

(Mrs. Coe stirs and opens her eyes.)

MRS. COE—Why hello, Doctor Campbell!

LITTLE OLD MAN—Hello, Mary.

(He hands the chicken bone to the nurse, who dips it in alcohol and passes it to Doctor Clarke.)

DOCTOR CLARKE *(examining the bone intently)*— Hmm, Wyandotte. Fenway will be interested in this. His birds are Wyandottes, I understand.

The Man in 32

I AM GLAD THAT PHYSICIANS HAVE DECIDED TO USE numbers, instead of names, to designate diseases. Of course, the hospitals are not sure yet that it will work, but hospitals are never sure of anything except that it is daybreak. Hospitals always know when daybreak comes and I think they will probably also welcome the new idea of numbering diseases, as it will be a great boon to nurses, internes, and orderlies, none of whom can write legibly.

All treatment of disease depends in large part on misunderstanding. To treat a malady successfully there must be a complete, not simply a partial, misunderstanding between doctors and nurses.

For instance, let us say that you are in Room 32 of a hospital, suffering from cirrhosis of the liver (sometimes called "American insides"). Cirrhosis of the liver will, under the new system, have a number—let us say 1352. This is an unlucky number because of the 13, but if you have cirrhosis of the liver you are unlucky already and the number won't make any difference. Now—let us say that the gentleman in Room 83 on the same floor has a bad case of chilblains which he picked up at the Ice Club, or, in medical parlance, he has 32. To complete the picture, the head nurse on the floor makes eights that look like threes.

Remember, now, you are in Room 32 with cirrhosis of the liver (1352), and the other fellow, poor chap, is down the hall terribly sick with 32 (chilblains). Suddenly you think it would be nice to get yourself a drink of water at the cooler, so you get out of bed and wander down the hall in your dressing gown, which should be deep purple, almost black. You meet a doctor, halfway. He says:

"Are you the man with 32?"

"Yes," you reply, thinking that he said are you the man *in* 32.

"What are you doing up?" says the doctor.

"I am on my way to get a drink of water," say you, little realizing that even if you could get one, it would be your last.

"A drink of water?" says the doctor in great astonishment, as though he had never heard of water, as many doctors haven't. "I will fix *you*! I will show you whether a man who feels as bad as you do can have a drink of water!" So saying, the doctor hastily scribbles something on a pad and calls the head nurse. The doctor has written: "3 teaspoonful of ZG/QR2 in tumbler of water 3 times a day, for 32."

The nurse, who not only makes eights that look like threes, but reads threes as though they were eights, gets eight teaspoonfuls of this stuff that is so wonderful for chilblains but which happens to be the worst thing in the world for cirrhosis of the liver, and she gives it to you in a tumbler of water not three times a day, mind you, but eight times a day, also leaving instructions for the night nurse to do the same thing, and the night nurse does.

Do I need to say any more to convince you that you are now dead? And need I say how sorry I am?

IV. Trials of Man, Who Inherited the Earth

Baby's First Step

I RECEIVED A CALL THIS MORNING FROM A MR. Aiken. He came to my apartment unheralded—a tall gray fellow, up from the warm street into my littered room.

"I am Mr. Aiken," he said, as he gained the top step. That was how I knew he was Mr. Aiken.

"Come in, Mr. Aiken," I replied.

Now before I go on to report this friendly call, I should tell the reader—whose interest in the whole matter I can merely assume, just as Mr. Aiken assumed that I was interested in life insurance—that just prior to the unexpected arrival of Mr. Aiken, I had released Baby, my small singing bird, from his cage for his morning constitutional. Baby was in the bathroom, going over the plumbing, when my guest entered.

Mr. Aiken sat down in the green chair and put his briefcase on the floor. I sat down on the piano stool.

"I understand," said Mr. Aiken, quietly, "that you are a writer. Is that correct?"

"No," I said.

"Well," continued Mr. Aiken, "that won't make any difference."

"To whom?"

"Well, I mean, that although my work is mostly among literary people—because, I suppose, I feel a sort of kinship for them although not making any pretensions of writing myself—although, as I say, my work is mostly among artists and writers, my profession—for life insurance *is* a profession—extends of course to all classes."

I offered Mr. Aiken a cigarette, which he didn't take.

"I suppose," he went on, "that to you I am just another life-insurance agent?"

"No. You are the first."

"Ah," said Mr. Aiken, straightening a little in his chair, "that is interesting. In that event" (here Mr. Aiken leaned over toward his briefcase), "in that event I would like to show you . . ."

As Mr. Aiken raised his briefcase, Baby, tiring of the bathroom, came winging in to join us. In his flight he passed just east of Mr. Aiken's face, side-slipping as he came. Mr. Aiken ducked.

"Ah," he said, amiably, "a bird!"

"A bird," I replied, watching Baby alight on the piano, next to a photograph of a lady whom we both admire.

"Well, now," said Mr. Aiken (Baby hopped to the edge of the piano and cleared his throat), "you can see, if you will glance at this chart, quicker than words can tell, just what my story is. This is made out on the basis of fifty thousand dollars merely for the purpose of . . ."

A low, liquid trill, to me a familiar and rather sweet sound, began to bubble into the air. Baby was commencing.

"Ah," said Mr. Aiken, looking up from the chart, "quite a singer!"

"Just beginning," I answered.

"Well, as I say, this is made out on the basis of . . . Oh, first may I ask whether you are married?"

"I am not."

"And your age is?" Mr. Aiken raised his voice to make it carry above Baby's.

"Twenty-nine."

"Well, then, let us say that you deposit . . ." Mr. Aiken rose slowly and came toward me, with the chart. He bent over slightly, so I could see the paper, whereupon Baby, a little bit incensed that his prelude had been interrupted, hopped down from the piano onto my guest's shoulder, mistaking it for just anything at all. Mr. Aiken, taken off his guard, stopped talking, held his pose breathlessly, and made a thin attempt to smile.

"He . . . er . . . won't . . . I mean, it's all right, is it, do you think?" asked Mr. Aiken.

"Yes. Just hold perfectly still," I said. "Just don't move, and don't talk."

Mr. Aiken obeyed. For about a minute he stood there, bird on shoulder, completely dumb and considerably worried. I rose and helped myself to another cigarette. Then I sat down again.

"Auhuh ahuh," said Mr. Aiken, and Baby moved on, taking up a position on a low bookshelf near the open window. Mr. Aiken resumed his seat.

"Let us say that you will deposit sixteen hundred dollars a year for . . ." Again that low, watery trill floated out across the room, this time rising and swelling into a rich sylvan hymn of praise for the day, continuing with a few disagreeable urban crescendos that Baby has lately developed in an attempt to prostitute his art and show off, the whole song making, in its flow and intensity, such a lively din in the place that conversation was unbearable and the thread of Mr. Aiken's discourse was again lost.

"He . . . the bird can't get out that open window, can he?" asked Mr. Aiken hopefully, when the song ceased.

"He can, but he won't," I replied.

"Oh. Now, with this yearly rate in the case of an unmarried man—and may I say that a young man must always look ahead to the time when he is *not* insurable, as well as to the time when he gets married and has beneficiaries . . ."

Surfeited with the view from the window, Baby did three laps around the room, stunting as he went, banking vertically around some imaginary pylons that he has erected for his amusement, and settling finally on his cage. Mr. Aiken watched, appalled at the spectacle.

". . . gets married and has beneficiaries," he continued, a trifle vaguely, "why then . . ."

Baby, at that moment, spying his own shadow on the wall, threw himself upon it viciously, and set up a loud vengeful screaming.

". . . gets married and has beneficiaries," Mr.

Aiken repeated, louder, "gets married and has beneficiaries . . . why, then . . . Excuse me, does that bird *always* knock his head against the wall that way?"

"Only in the late spring of the year."

"As I say, when you get married . . ."

Later that morning, when Mr. Aiken had gone and I was just hanging round with nothing much to do, and not covered by insurance, I gave Baby a small helping of the special tonic he is so fond of.

Now That I'm Organized

It will be a week come tomorrow that Miss Nulty looked up from her dictation and said: "You have no work-organizer on your desk, have you, Mr. White?"

Seven crowded days have intervened. I can hardly believe that at this time last week I did not even know what a work-organizer was.

"You see," said Miss Nulty, returning from the stock room with a package under her arm, "now instead of having your papers strewn all over your desk, you place them in this organizer under the proper headings, where you can always find them quick." Then, seeing my embarrassment, she considerately left the room, and I was alone with my work-organizer.

I lit a cigarette. The new article was brown, and very cleverly constructed—a sort of flat paper file, with twelve flaps, each flap fitted with a small isinglass frame in which the person whose work was to be organized could insert a "heading" or "classification." It did not take me long to realize that the first step would be to organize the organizer.

Cutting the little strips of paper for the frames took quite a while and was light, pleasant work. Thinking up headings, however, did not come so easily. I decided to devote the first compartment to Beazley & Hoke, to whom we sell most of our harness snaps, and with whom, for that reason, I have a great deal of correspondence. I lettered the name on one of the strips of paper and inserted it in the first frame. It showed up well, although my capital B was never anything to go around telling people about. The second flap I called "Letters to Answer."

Next it occurred to me that there should be one compartment in my organizer given over to matters that demanded immediate attention. I wrote out "Matters Demanding Immediate Attention"— but it was too long to fit the little isinglass frame, and didn't have quite the right sound anyway. I tried shortening it to "Immediate Attention Things" and then to "Right Away Papers," but neither of these seemed to have the authentic tone. By this time the strain of trying to invent headings was making me a little bit sick, and I had to leave my desk for a moment and get a drink of water. It worried me to be showing signs of nerves—here it was eleven o'clock, my desk piled high, and no work done. Still, I thought, once I get this organizer going I certainly will be able to tear through this stuff.

When I returned from the water-cooler I settled on the word "Quick" as the best heading for the third compartment. Just before inserting it, another thought came to me, and I took my pen and added an exclamation point, making it "Quick!" It looked fine.

Before another hour was over I had reserved a compartment for Mr. Higgins, one for "Unimportant," one for "To Think About," one called "Yes or No?" (in which I decided to put matters which might come to me for my opinion, although there are not many of these), and then I remembered that after all it was Miss Nulty who had got the work-organizer for me and the least I could do to show my appreciation would be to name one of the compartments for her.

I called the ninth "Personal," the tenth "Loose Papers," and then, with two compartments still unnamed, my imagination refused to budge. This bothered me, for I decided that there would be no vacant compartments in a desk file of mine. For a time I didn't know but that I would have to close my desk and go home and lie down there for a while.

Finally, despairing, I named one of the flaps "Cigarette Coupons" and destroyed the twelfth (and last) one by ripping out the flap and throwing it away.

It was now past one o'clock, and I went to lunch.

How clearly the events of that day stand out in my memory! I recall perfectly picking up the menu at the restaurant and seeing, instead of items of food, a bill which read like this:

BEAZLEY & HOKE
LETTERS TO ANSWER
QUICK!
MR. HIGGINS
UNIMPORTANT
TO THINK ABOUT
YES OR NO?
MISS NULTY
PERSONAL
LOOSE PAPERS
CIGARETTE COUPONS

"Beef stew," I told the waiter—but I could do no more than pick at it. On my way back to the office I bought a pack of cigarettes. A few moments later,

when I thought no one was looking, I slid the coupons in the right compartment and felt a whole
lot of relief at having taken the first step toward
filling up the organizer. Still, even with that as a
starter, the task proved to be only in its infancy.

All afternoon things got steadily worse. Almost
every paper on my desk seemed to admit of more
than one classification, and I have never been able
to make quick decisions. Here, for example, was
a letter from Mr. Hoke. First I pushed it tenta-
tively under "Beazley & Hoke," only to withdraw
it hurriedly and put it under "Letters to Answer."
There again I wasn't sure of myself. I remembered that it was probably a pretty urgent letter
and therefore should be under "Quick!" I made
that change. Unfortunately, in filing it, I happened to glance at it and saw how very urgent it
really was. It was so urgent that it should have
been acknowledged by phone at ten o'clock in the
morning, and here it was three in the afternoon
and the letter just being filed under "Quick!"
Heaven knew when I would get round to looking
under "Quick!" For an instant I wavered and was
tempted to tend to the letter directly; but I knew
how fatal to any work-organizer system it would

be were I to start acting that way. I was thoroughly
frightened, now. It was no longer possible for me
to remain seated; the phone rang intermittently,
the distribution boy appeared at intervals with
new memoranda and letters, and I saw only too
clearly that I was not even holding my own—the
desk was littered worse than when I started. In
my panicky condition I went about picking up
pieces of paper, with a vague garbled expression
on my face—picking them up, laying them down
again, and all the while walking slowly round and
round my desk. I was ten minutes trying to decide
whether to put a circular letter from my university's endowment fund under "Unimportant" or
"To Think About." That's how bad I was. At four
o'clock, echoes from my inactive, distraught state
began to be heard. The first was an inquiry from
the office of our first vice-president, wanting to
know why I hadn't sent a confirmation of Beazley
& Hoke's order of even date for five thousand harness snaps. After twenty minutes' frantic search
I found the order under "Loose Papers," refiled
it under "Quick!" and sent back a memorandum
to the vice-president, saying: "Everything in good
time."

When the news of the second echo arrived, I was in the reception-room, lying on the couch, the blood pumping in my head. Miss Nulty brought me the tidings. It seems that in one of the letters on my desk there had been a P.S., stating that Mr. Beazley himself would be in New York on Thursday, and would our Mr. Higgins care to see him for lunch and possibly for a little golf? "Don't you know that is very important?" asked Miss Nulty, trying to speak gently.

"Yes," I replied, wearily, "where did you find it?"

"In the bottom of your work-organizer," she replied, "in amongst a couple of cigarette coupons!"

Well, as I say, seven crowded days have intervened since I got my work-organizer. On the whole it has been a happy period. Things have gradually smoothed out, and I am glad to say that it still takes me the entire day, from nine to five, to organize my work, with the gratifying result that I never have to do any.

The Doily Menace

MY TROUBLE WITH DOILIES DATES WAY BACK. I WAS a child when they first started to bother me. Now, having attained my full growth, I still suffer from them.

The first real difficulty came as a result of my not knowing what the word doily meant. I heard it used around the house, but, as sometimes happens, I did not immediately connect the object with the word. Result: I concluded that doilies had something to do with sex, which frightened me. (Whenever, as a child, I failed to understand words, I attributed the fact to my ignorance of sexology. Doily was a word made for the purpose— it sounded a little bit shady, and sex, if you remember, was shady up until about 1919.) So I went around not daring to ask my mother what a doily was. I didn't dare ask her about babies; why should I ask her about doilies?

The dictionary was no help, because I thought doily was spelled "doylee." As I look back, the dictionary seems to have helped me very little in

any of my troubles. Ours was a Webster's mounted
on a tripod in a room called "Albert's room," and
it was pretty evasive about the words that interested me most. I let doily go as a bad job. Maybe,
I reasoned, it was such a dirty word they couldn't
even put it in the dictionary.

The next doily trouble I had came in my early
restaurant days. Of course, by that time I had
learned what doilies were, but I had not learned
to watch out for them. One evening I ate one. It
was a paper doily. It was served to me under a
slice of pie, in a restaurant in Eighth Street. The
restaurant was dimly lit, and I was young. I ate the
pie and the doily with it, dreamily forking it down,
uncritical and inattentive. Just as I was finishing I
discovered my mistake—a small paper fragment remained, a telltale trace, dog-eared and limp. I was
considerably upset. For about three days there-
after I kept expecting death. My thoughts, like
my stomach, were all disarranged and went round
in my head like little swirls of paper on city side-
walks in a windstorm. I could think only in
phrases, not sentences; phrases like "deadly cel-
lulose," "paper wadding," "traced to his having
once swallowed a foreign object," " made from old

rags." I felt miserable. I was quite sure that my doily was growing, inside me. Paper swells.

That episode ended at last. Things blew over. I forgot doilies in the mad pleasures of life as a young advertising man. Months, even years, rolled along, peaceably enough. My early fears had been dissipated, I was getting along better with sex, Havelock Ellis had come and gone, restaurants no longer bemused me to the extent that I ate their pastries paper and all, and—to make my happiness complete—Spring was again here. I remember it was a lovely night in early May that I was invited to dine at the home of a lady of such vast beauty and elegant demeanor that I trembled to think of my own good fortune.

I went. My hostess was a play-actress, and like all play-actresses she received me well and treated me with courtesy—even with, I thought, affection. Also, like all play-actresses, she was to serve cocoa-nut-cream pudding for dessert. I knew, of course, that it was coming, and I was ready.

My dessert plate came on, a transparent glass plate. On it was a finger bowl. I was ready for that, too. "My lovely hostess," I thought to myself, "can't make a simpleton out of me simply by

serving a finger bowl on a dessert plate." Quite
casually I removed the finger-bowl, set it to one
side, leaving the dessert plate free to receive the
dessert when it should be passed.

Free? Yes, I thought that. Reader, it looked like
a free plate to me. Even while I was helping myself to spoonful after spoonful of delicious cocoa-
nut-cream pudding, it looked like a free plate to
me. Not till a moment later, when I dug down
with my fork and brought up out of the soggy
depths a fine Italian linen doily, saturated, as only
an Italian linen doily can be, with pudding, did I
realize how far from free the plate had been.

I stared, fascinated, at the dripping doily. From
its delicate interstices little yellow morsels of pudding oozed. Slowly I raised my eyes and looked up
at my sweet hostess smiling at me across the table.

There was a pause.

"Better put it down," she said.

Without a moment's wait, I raised the doily to
my mouth and swallowed it at a single gulp.

"Cheero," I replied. "Down it is."

The Key of Life

ONE OF THE PEOPLE AFFECTED BY ENGLAND'S suspension of the gold standard was Henry C. Earp, who didn't understand what it meant. He simply knew that the news made him feel queer. He read it on his way to work, riding down on the El. The El made Mr. Earp sick in the early morning anyway: this morning the combination of England's crisis and the train's motion gave him the sort of indigestion that is part fear and part jiggling.

There had been so much talk about bad times; Mr. Earp had even heard the words "revolution" and "panic." Those words came back to him. Here was England, suspending the gold standard. That might mean anything. It might mean (Mr. Earp said the word softly to himself) "everything." Through his head there flashed a succession of cataclysmic events—fighting in the streets, mill riots, fire, bank failures, dissolution of all the things that made a civilized people. He trembled as the El train rattled along. What if everything were really coming to an end? Suppose the dollar should drop in value till it was just so much paper —where would he be? Quite possibly the only survivors would be persons who owned their own land and grew their own food and made their own clothes out of the skins of animals. Mr. Earp allowed his mind to rest, for a fleeting moment, on the possibility of his shooting an animal and making a suit of clothes from the skin.

He also ran over in his mind the years that had flown by, the eighteen years that he had been pleased to regard as his business career. His really wasn't a career at all. He had never made any money, had merely held his job. The Little Birdseye Furniture Company hadn't advanced him, nor had they fired him. He ran the tickler cards in their credit department; he knew which installment customers to dun and which to let alone. Eighteen years had taught him the exact moment at which to call up and say that the Company would send its truck to take away the davenport unless a substantial payment were made. But he hadn't actually advanced any; and now, while England tottered, he was still making thirty-two dollars a week. Maybe in a week's time thirty-two dollars wouldn't be worth the paper it was printed on. Mr. Earp was thoroughly frightened.

A few minutes before he arrived at his station, he happened to glance again at his newspaper, and his eye lit on an advertisement that won his close attention. A man was going to lecture that night at Carnegie Hall, on "Making Your Life a Supreme Success." He would divulge business secrets and tell *how to get ahead seven times faster*. It was to be a free lecture, Mr. Earp noticed. Another sub-head challenged him: "Excuse-finders not wanted; if you think the depression is going to last forever, we can't help you!"

Mr. Earp liked the tone of that. Somebody, at any rate, wasn't scared. The train stopped and he got out and walked to the office, his stomach still bothering him.

That evening, at 8:15, he was at Carnegie Hall. He found a balcony, and sat there, in the half-seat high in the topmost section of the darkness, hold-ing, with some embarrassment, the little folder the usher had handed him, "Making Your Life a Su-preme Success." The hall was crowded. This fel-low must be pretty good. Mr. Earp looked about, shyly, at the people around him. Some were men his own age, behind whose pale brows rested the neat and tired brain of the desk worker. Some were young couples, obviously searching for life's key. He saw a white-haired man of seventy, blind in one eye. He saw a colored man with a carnation in his buttonhole. All were eagerly staring down toward the far-away stage where the Success Builder, in evening dress, was beginning his talk. Mr. Earp glanced nervously through the little folder. There were pictures of the successful graduates of the Complete Course, now out in life making good: happy branch managers, happy sales executives answering busy telephones, happy captains of field artillery, and one happy old lady who had commercialized her fruit cake at the age of sixty-one. There were letters of congratulation from the governors of states, and there were extracts from newspapers quoting the speaker as an authority on business. At the end there was a coupon to be filled out by those who wished to "go on" to the real twelve-part twenty-dollar course; and a money-back guarantee for the unsatisfied.

Earp was excited. The crowded hall, the sense of being on the verge of something, set his blood going. Again he felt sick, but this time it was the nausea of renascent hope. He was listening to a big man, a man who had made good, a man who wasn't worried about the gold standard. Earp collected his attention.

"The world," he heard the great voice say, "is full of good things, and you can live a full life, every one of you. But my friends has it ever occurred to you that the people who get the good things in this world are the people who have been *trained* to get them? Why, I was reading only the other day about the star players of the Notre Dame team, coming back for fall practice. You might ask: Why should last year's football stars have to practice for the 1931 season—why don't they sit back and take it easy? My friends, I'll tell you why: It's because this is 1931, not 1930. And next year will be 1932, and I say to you that if you go into 1932 with a 1931 mind, then you will deserve to fail!"

Mr. Earp gripped his seat. This man was talking a man's language, no vague nonsense.

"Now another thing," continued the speaker, "you've all heard a great deal of loose talk about the depression. A man came to me the other day and said he'd been to a crystal gazer, and the crystal gazer had said to him: 'Don't start anything till after the first of April.' My friends, *I* say that any-body who postpones his plans for six months will forget he ever wanted anything."

There was a ripple of applause, in which Mr. Earp, tucking his folder under an arm, joined. When the applause faded, the speaker read a poem called "When I appreciate you and you appreciate me," and then took up, one by one, the twelve "tool" subjects that would be covered in the Coaching Course: How You Can Win Immediate Advancement; How to Acquire Popularity, Poise, and Power; How to Express Yourself to Win; and so on. The speaker's voice was becoming richer, more emotional. He told pertinent story after pertinent story, parable after parable, all pointing the same moral. Earp's eyes glistened. He chuckled at the stories, nodded his head wisely at the para-bles. This was the greatest lecture he had ever heard.

It was getting late, and the speaker went into his conclusion—a long story about his childhood. When he was a child, farmers always stored apples in their cellars in winter. Some of the apples were good apples, and some were specked apples; and when he, as a little boy, used to go down cellar he was always told to bring up the specked apples for eating, otherwise they would spoil. But of course there was always a new lot of specked apples every time, so the result was that his family went all winter eating the specked apples, never eating the good apples. "My friends," he said, "there are hundreds of men and women in this great auditorium tonight (and I regret that so many other hundreds had to be turned away at the door) who are leading specked-apple lives! Are *you* leading a specked-apple life? I say to you that the world is full of good things, and you who are content to eat specked apples because you don't *know enough* to eat the good ones are losing the richest joys of this great, rich, abundant earth."

The applause was heavy. Mr. Earp rose with the others. His legs felt strong under him. He had forgotten England and her sorrow, forgotten the Little Birdseye Furniture Company. This was a different world—a gorgeous place of lights, people, and intimations of big events. He was at the stairs. As he began the long slow descent to the lobby, his exhilaration was almost unbearable. The people in his path seemed to block him, prevent him from getting started.

At the bottom of the first flight of steps, a young man with curly black hair turned casually to him and said: "The same old boloney, eh?"

Mr. Earp swallowed. He nodded weakly, without looking at the youth.

"Success stuff is always the bunk," continued the young man. "It's all in getting a break. A corporation doesn't recognize an individual."

"Sure, I know it," said Earp, a trifle sullenly.

"What a bunch of horsefeathers that guy spilled —all them jokes about specked apples and all that junk!"

"I'll say," said Earp. His tone was more positive.

They descended another flight, slow step by slow step. The curly headed youth still stuck to him. "I'm sorry for the saps that fall for a spellbinder like him, and pay good money for the course."

"You and me, brother," said Earp, with a slight vocal swagger.

They reached the lobby, and passed quickly by the desks where people were signing up for the twenty-dollar complete course of twelve steps that

would enable them to become successful in business. At the sidewalk, the two parted. Earp crossed
Fifty-seventh Street and got on a bus. The conductor, noticing that he had come from the lecture,
nodded his head toward Carnegie Hall.

"You been in there?"

"Sure," said Earp.

"How was it? Did that feller tell you anything?"

Mr. Earp was halfway up the stairs to the upper
deck of the bus. He turned, sagely. "The usual
horsefeathers," he replied.

Obituary

DAISY ("BLACK WATCH DEBATABLE") DIED DE-
cember 22, 1931, when she was hit by a Yellow
cab in University Place. At the moment of her
death she was smelling the front of a florist's shop.
It was a wet day, and the cab skidded up over the
curb—just the sort of excitement that would have
amused her, had she been at a safe distance. She is
survived by her mother, Jeannie; a brother, Ab-
ner; her father, whom she never knew; and two
sisters, whom she never liked. She was three years
old.

Daisy was born at 65 West Eleventh Street in a
clothes closet at two o'clock of a December morning in 1928. She came, as did her sisters and brothers, as an unqualified surprise to her mother, who
had for several days previously looked with a low-
grade suspicion on the box of bedding that had
been set out for the delivery, and who had gone
into the clothes closet merely because she had felt
funny and wanted a dark, awkward place to feel
funny in. Daisy was the smallest of the litter of
seven, and the oddest.

Her life was full of incident but not of accomplishment. Persons who knew her only slightly regarded her as an opinionated little bitch, and said so; but she had a small circle of friends who saw through her, cost what it did. At Speyer Hospital, where she used to go when she was indisposed, she was known as "Whitey," because, the man told me, she was black. All her life she was subject to moods, and her feeling about horses laid her sanity open to question. Once she slipped her leash and chased a horse for three blocks through heavy traffic, in the carking belief that she was an effective agent against horses. Drivers of teams, seeing her only in the moments of her delirium, invariably leaned far out of their seats and gave tongue, mocking her; and thus made themselves even more ridiculous, for the moment, than Daisy.

She had a stoical nature, and spent the latter part of her life an invalid, owing to an injury to her right hind leg. Like many invalids, she developed a rather objectionable cheerfulness, as though to deny that she had cause for rancor. She also developed, without instruction or encouragement, a curious habit of holding people firmly by the ankle without actually biting them—a habit that gave her an immense personal advantage and won her many enemies. As far as I know, she never even broke the thread of a sock, so delicate was her grasp (like a retriever's), but her point of view was questionable, and her attitude was beyond explaining to the person whose ankle was at stake. For my own amusement, I often tried to diagnose this quirkish temper, and I think I understand it: she suffered from a chronic perplexity, and it relieved her to take hold of something.

She was arrested once, by Patrolman Porko. She enjoyed practically everything in life except motoring, an exigency to which she submitted silently, without joy, and without nausea. She never grew up, and she never took pains to discover, conclusively, the things that might have diminished her curiosity and spoiled her taste. She died sniffing life, and enjoying it.

An Evening on Ice

WITH THE COMING OF THE THAW, A MELANCHOLY fell upon me, for the ice went out from the Park, and I was fat with no skating. The evenings grew somber, with warm noises and the drip from the eaves. When I could endure it no longer I packed skates under arm and went where people told me to go—for they said plainly there was a public skating rink in Madison Square Garden.

Now in many of my waking hours I am full of sad dreams and dim excursions, so that I go about with no thought for what I am doing with myself.

Thus gently dreaming, I approached Madison Square Garden. Seeing an entrance, I went in. Seeing a ticket window, I purchased a ticket. Seeing a ticket-taker, I handed him what I had bought. Seeing a throng of people, I went along with them.

And seeing an opening before me, I strode giddily on, my skates under my arm, into the very heart of a large exposition called "Own Your Own Home."

"Friend," said a voice, "don't go round picking

up your clothes out of your neighbor's yard: simply hoist your wash to the ceiling on a Butler Clothes Dryer." I looked, and there, directly in front of me, was a clothes dryer being hoisted up on a little pulley by the man. It worked, I thought, very well.

"It works very well," I said, in a small voice. Then I moved away quickly and sought to tuck my skates out of sight.

All around me, I noticed, were people interested in homes. There were little heart-shaped signs which said: Home—the Heart of the Nation. A young man sauntered past, a girl on his arm. Then another couple. I looked around: as far as I could see along the crowded aisles were couples: boy and girl together, man and wife, two and two. It was a very pretty sight.

I, too, had often thought I would like to have a home.

"This is buckwheat coal," said a man. I walked on. The sound of a 'cello came sweetly through the hum of voices, and I began to feel strangely moved by the sight of so many devices contributing to household peace. Still gently dreaming, I walked dimly among vacuum cleaners, underground garbage receivers, built-in bookcases, bathroom utility cabinets, oak flooring, electric refrigerators, formal gardens, and little knives for slicing slaw. I wanted to be happy. Every man wants to be happy. And here, in this place, every man but me had a girl on his arm.

A pair of ice skates for me; a girl for other men. People were noticing me, wondering.

How long I wandered through the bright aisles I can not now recall to mind.

And what compelled me to halt finally before a booth where a girl was demonstrating magic silver polish, I shall never know.

She was dipping tarnished spoons into a pan of water, from which they were shortly to emerge shiny.

As I stood there, watching her hands, the purposeless character of my life was strong upon me; my years hung heavy round my head; my mawkishness, my irresponsible way of living bore me down, and I saw that all my futilities, all my willingness to go alone in the world, making small progress, had led at last to the woebegone spectacle of a dismal man, standing, ice-skates under his arm, in front of a silver polish booth!

Tears came flooding forth, and with them the

desire to change my life and give it the richness it deserved.

The little crowd had dispersed; the silver polish girl was quite alone among her utensils. She, alone; I, alone.

I approached the booth. "Do you skate?" I asked softly.

Growing Up in New Canaan

IT BELONGS TO SOME PEOPLE NAMED SPILLWAY,"
said Mrs. White. "Mr. Spillway is a writer."

We were talking about a house that we were
driving out to look at. Mrs. White and I often
drive out and look at houses on Sunday afternoon,
feeling that there is no more stimulating pastime
than snooping through other people's homes and
commenting on the thousand and one little objec-
tions that we find to living in them.

"Did Mr. Spillway tell you how to get to the
house, or is he simply a writer?" I asked.

"I know how to find it," said Mrs. White. "It's
three miles out of New Canaan on a road, and it
has a concrete-mixer in the front yard."

"And a family of wrens in the concrete-mixer?"
I added, enthusiastically. "Did you know that
wrens only build in concrete-mixers that face
northeast? And six weeks after the first eggs have
hatched, the mother wren is at it again and lays
another clutch."

We drove on for a while in the silence that usually follows humorous or informative remarks of that sort, and I kept wondering what the Spillways were doing with a concrete-mixer in the front yard. "What are the Spillways doing with a concrete-mixer in the front yard?" I finally asked.

"They have been adding on to the house."

We turned left on what Mrs. White called the "road," and in the course of the afternoon did come upon the Spillway house; and there, just as stated, was the concrete-mixer. It wasn't exactly *in* the front yard, the front yard being a thing of the past, having been absorbed by the contractor. There were some traces of yard left, notably a bush, but the main body of it had been removed. Inside the house a painter was at work painting a wall, even though it was Sunday.

"Where are the Spillways?" I asked him.

"They ain't here."

"It's their house, isn't it?"

"Sure, but they're living down the road in another house. They'll be here any moment, though. You can look around if you want."

We soon found ourselves prying happily into the various rooms of the Spillway house—both the old section and the new addition. It was indeed a fine

place, and we were in the midst of panning it
loudly to each other when we were joined by the
owners themselves, Mr. and Mrs. Spillway, whom
I liked instantly. Mr. Spillway had brought along
a bottle of whiskey: he was holding it dreamily in
his hand as though he had forgotten to put it
down. He and I followed Mrs. White and Mrs.
Spillway at a little distance as the four of us wandered about through the treacherous corridors and
dank sunrooms. It soon became apparent to me
that the addition to the house had been Mrs.
Spillway's idea, and that it had been achieved in a
devilish clever fashion by gouging out the land in
the rear and throwing it to one side, against the
garage. I noticed, as we strolled about, that Mr.
Spillway looked at everything with a sort of remi-
niscent curiosity and affection, bestowing on
rooms, walls, and alterations a glance such as one
sometimes gives one's child in a moment of ob-
jectivity, when one wonders how it all came about
anyway. Several times he stopped and stared into
a fireplace or at a door, as though he had never
seen it before; and once I caught him staring peace-
fully into space, as though gazing at something that
had been.

"This is the studio," said Mrs. Spillway, up ahead, entering a long white room, "where Mr. Spillway will do his work. Unless, of course, we sell." She smiled back at us men.

Mr. Spillway was still regarding everything with the same quiet, curious amazement. "What did she just say?" he asked.

"Said this was where you'd work," I whispered.

"You know what that means, I guess," he said. "Means this is where I'll sit with a couple of cronies, and drink."

I nodded.

"We might have one now," he murmured sadly, recalling the bottle of whiskey he held in his hand.

"Let's," I said. And we sat down on some old planks and drank quietly. Through the new French doors we could see the destruction out back, where the contractor had scored a direct hit. A few small trees remained of what had once been a wood.

"See that out there?" said my host. "Used to be all covered with violets in the spring." His eye came to rest on a wheelbarrow heavily encrusted with mortar. The ladies had gone upstairs, and we could hear Mrs. Spillway telling Mrs. White about

a new door that had been knocked through between rooms, to save a person from going out into
the hall. "We used to have to go out into the hall,"
we heard her say, "and it was a perfect nuisance."

"Wasn't bad," said my host softly, to me. "I
didn't mind going out into the hall. I sometimes
like going out into the hall. Gives you a change of
scene. You know?"

I nodded, and pointed to the whiskey. "We
might have another."

"Let's," said my host. After a minute or two he
turned to me solemnly. "Listen," he said. "Want
some fun? Ask to see the furnace." Again I nodded
my head. We rose and joined the ladies in a bathroom.

"I was wondering," I said to Mrs. Spillway, who
was standing in the tub to make more room for the
rest of us, "whether I might see the furnace."

She stepped quickly out of the tub, giving her
husband a glance. "It's an oil-burner. They're the
most marvellous things! We can go down this way,
through the studio." Mrs. Spillway led us down,
and out into the ruined yard. "The furnace is in
the garage," she explained. "They always put them
away from the house, for safety. And I want to tell

you something funny that has happened to this one while the work has been going on here this winter."

"Don't tell them!" put in Mr. Spillway. "Let 'em look."

We entered the garage. In one corner of the concrete floor was a large pit, about six feet square and six feet deep, full to the brim of water. Sticking up above the surface, its gauge awash, its copper pipes disappearing into the cool depths, was an oil-burner.

"See it?" said Mr. Spillway, pointing.

For a while nobody said anything. It was a spectacle that one looked at, not talked about.

"How the deuce did it happen?" I finally asked, thinking that that might be the thing to say about a furnace that had foundered.

"Well," replied Mrs. Spillway, gaily, "when they built the pit, they left a hole down there so that the outlet pipe could be cleaned if it ever got clogged, and they forgot that water could come *in* when we changed the level of the yard. It's really a scream, isn't it? I called up the oil-burner people and they said water wouldn't hurt it any."

Long after the ladies had gone from the garage,

Mr. Spillway and myself lingered on in the pleasant dampness, gazing down amiably into the brown waters of the furnace hole. "Want to know something else funny?" said Mr. Spillway after a while. His face again wore that rapt air of affectionate search. "It's true about the water."

"What do you mean?" I asked.

"About the water not hurting it. I investigated for myself. You wouldn't believe it, but it's perfectly true that water doesn't hurt the god-damn thing."

Journey's Dead-End

MR. WEISKOPF WORKED FOR BANDLER, GARDNER, Bushwick & Klein, and the thing he hated most was the reception room. Anything, it seemed to him, might happen in the reception room. Usually it was something dismal, although occasionally it was something alarming.

The reception room was large, and was ineffectually divided into nooks by unattractive screens. This was for the purpose of keeping clients segregated. Bandler, Gardner, Bushwick & Klein handled the advertising for about sixteen concerns, whose interests by no means coincided. It was best to keep them screened off when they called. To Mr. Weiskopf the awful hazard of the reception room was its uncertainty: you had to take most callers sight unseen. Even when someone whom you knew was announced, you could never tell who else would be sitting there behind screens, waiting and listening.

On the particular day of which I am writing, Mr. Weiskopf's phone rang and the girl at the reception desk said: "Mr. Nathan is in the reception room to see you."

"All right," said Mr. Weiskopf, "I'll be out."

He hung up the phone and allowed his head to sink down in the cradle of his arm. Nathan was his bootlegger, and was one of the most dismal of all dismal callers. Nathan opened every conversation with "Hello, Colonel!" Today, Mr. Weiskopf thought to himself, it would be more than he could endure to go out into the reception room and answer to the title Colonel. The world was changing, old values had been displaced, people were thinking about serious affairs, no one had the strength to reply to "Hello, Colonel!" any more. Yet he knew he ought to go out and see Nathan, because he wanted some rye. There was no hurry, though.

As he sat, bent with woe, there passed through Mr. Weiskopf's head, in mournful procession, all the people who had ever come into that reception room. Agents. Dealers. Artists. A lady in a double-breasted, white piqué vest. College chums. Clients. Clients with blood in their eye. Clients wanting to go out and have some fun, at Bandler, Gardner, Bushwick & Klein's expense. Photographers' models. Applicants for jobs. Nuns. Contraltos. Wrens. National secretaries of fraternities. Girl Scouts

People with dachshunds in leash. Deaf people.
(The screens were so much paper, when deaf people arrived.) A young man with a stack of card-
board boxes eight feet high. The procession went
on and on. Mr. Weiskopf thought regretfully
about all the money he had lent these people, all
the miserable times he had had with them. The
lady in the white piqué vest had carried a stick; he
thought of that, too.

Wearily he raised his head, remembering that
Nathan was waiting. He got up, and went to the
reception room. He peeked skilfully behind all
the screens. There were two men in the room.
Neither was Nathan. The old feeling of alarm and
disgust began to steal over Mr. Weiskopf. He
wandered out to the reception desk and asked the
girl where Nathan was. "In there," she said. "It's
not the Nathan that usually comes, though. It's
another one."

Another one, thought Mr. Weiskopf. The parade grows always longer. He reëntered the reception room. Throwing a quick glance around, he
picked the man who seemed the lesser of the two
evils. "Mr. Nathan?" he asked, with gloomy politeness.

The man rose, slowly. He was a tall, quiet man.

with dark eyes and apparent sincerity of purpose. He wore a long black overcoat with a velvet collar. Narrowing his eyes, he stared at Mr. Weiskopf as though he saw him indistinctly. Then he said, softly: "Mr. Weiskopf?"

"Yes."

"Mr. A. C. Weiskopf?"

"Yes."

There was a pause. The caller seemed dissatisfied, incredulous. He stepped closer to Mr. Weiskopf, rather too close, and looked steadily at Mr. Weiskopf's features. "That's funny," he said.

"What is?" asked Mr. Weiskopf.

"Why, you're not the Mr. Weiskopf I usually see when I come here."

"I'm not?"

"No."

"That *is* funny."

Mr. Weiskopf heard himself say "That *is* funny," but he didn't understand why he should have said it. He and his caller were standing so close together that Mr. Weiskopf, who was far-sighted, felt out of focus, unsteady. For another moment neither said anything. Then Mr. Nathan:

"You're sure you're Mr. Weiskopf?"

"Yes," replied Mr. Weiskopf, weakly. "There

used to be a fellow in our production department named Weiskopf, though. Maybe you're thinking of him."

"No," said Mr. Nathan. "Weiskopf. A. C. Weiskopf."

"Have you seen him—that is, me—many times, or just a couple of times?"

"Many times. I'm in here a good deal."

"Are you really?" said Mr. Weiskopf. He wished he could back away, to bring his caller into focus; but it would have seemed impolite. Again there was a pause.

"Well," said Mr. Nathan, slowly, "let's go at it another way: do I look familiar to you?"

"No, you don't."

"You've never seen me before?"

"No, I never have." Mr. Weiskopf realized, as he said the words, that he was only fairly sure of this. After all, Mr. Nathan looked not unlike several men he knew; but on the other hand, he knew those men well, would recognize them instantly, and their names wouldn't be Nathan. This chain of ideas increased his dizziness.

"It's really remarkable, isn't it?" said Mr. Nathan, swaying closer.

"Yes, it is," said Mr. Weiskopf, swaying. "To tell

you the truth, you're not the Mr. Nathan I came into the reception room expecting to find, either." This remark seemed to have echoes that sounded exquisitely irrelevant, almost rude. But his caller seemed perfectly willing to follow it up.

"I'm not?" said Mr. Nathan.

"No. This fellow Nathan whom I usually see doesn't look anything like you."

"You're sure?"

"Yes."

"Well, that puts me in a funny position, too."

"Yes, it does," said Mr. Weiskopf, somewhat sympathetically. He tried to frame the next question. Maybe it was foolish to ask any more questions; maybe they had better quit.

"When you come in here," continued Mr. Weiskopf, "what do you usually come in about?"

"About the Kul-Air Filter account."

"And you see a Mr. Weiskopf?"

"Yes."

"And I'm not Mr. Weiskopf?"

"No."

"I'll be darned," said Mr. Weiskopf, dreamily.

The two men hadn't moved an inch. Neither had raised his voice. Neither had been anything but friendly and sincere in his attempt to get on a working basis with the other. Each saw how utterly he had failed, how wide the gulf that separated them. At length Mr. Nathan broke the silence. "Well," he said, holding out his hand, "goodbye."

Mr. Weiskopf shook the hand. "Goodbye," he said, warmly.

Mr. Nathan walked out, tall and slow.

Liberal in a Lounge Car

THIS TRAIN (HE SAID TO THE MAN NEXT TO HIM) exactly suits my purposes. It's the only efficient way to go to Boston. I can wade through a pile of work in the morning, clear my desk by 10:30, give dictation, then put a battery of girls to work getting up the letters. Just before the train pulls out, my secretary, Birdsall, brings the whole wad of stuff aboard for signature, revision, and so forth. That was Birdsall you probably saw. I put through those that are O.K., and take the others along with me; then at Boston I have a public stenographer meet me and handle the load at the other end. I can integrate this train perfectly with my work schedule, and the food is good, too, if you treat the dining-car captain generously. Would you mind just pushing that button behind you, I'd like another highball. Thanks. Will you have a cigar? Here you are, boy. *Encore le* Scotch-and-Soda. Don't you know what *encore* means? Guess you didn't go to the right school. Well, just bring me another drink like a good fellow. And an afternoon paper, please.

I follow the Sino-Japanese crisis very closely. It's the crux of the present recession—even more than this man down in Washington. The absorption of China is inevitable, of course; but the amusing thing is the effect abroad, particularly in England. I've watched England losing ground for years now, and the implications, both in the Orient and in Spain, are highly significant as bearing on the gradual dissipation of England's imperial structure. Funny how few people realize the way England's going. It's really the most amusing development of the past two years. Naturally she bears the brunt of the Italian threat because of India. England knows perfectly well she'd never hold India in the event of serious trouble. I'd like more fizz, please, my boy. The next two years will see the lid blow off without question. I've been in England a good deal, and I think I can say honestly I understand the English temperament. It's appalling, what the last two years have seen.

Will you have a drink with me? I don't go for the hard stuff, ordinarily, but I'm beginning to feel this morning's extra pressure. Business is a tough egg these days, with empires falling and rising. You have to play ball, if you want the figures to come out right. Of course, the social experiment in this country is really an amazing thing. And a good thing. Most people don't grasp it, but I welcome it. The world is on the march, and if you don't believe me all you have to do is glance over these headlines. Spain. Italy. Russia. Japan. All turbulent. With England on the wane, and America holding the bag. All you hear in the business world is bellyaching; but I prefer to play ball. I have the best lawyers in the country helping me watch the curves as they come over the plate, and that's something. But even more than that is my mental attitude. You've got to be philosophical and you've got to have a liberal point of view in turn with the times. Hell, I welcome a recession such as this. It helps me understand myself better. And I play along with the boys in Washington. I've never been able to understand these liverish fellows who jump out of the window just because their arithmetic doesn't check. Why, a good friend of ours jumped in the crash of '29—a man worth three quarters of a million even after he'd been cleaned. A man who had everything to live for—lovely wife (a really swell person, I knew her extremely well) and two fine children. That's all that matters in life, anyway. I'm beginning to see things so much

clearer. Why should we pile up dough indefinitely?
Look here, I happen to have more than I want—
literally. That's not a boast, I'm just talking
straight to you. But listen. I've got five kids, and
that's my asset side of the ledger right there. Those
kids. I planned to have four, but my wife went off
the deep end and threw twins the last time, and I
tell you I wouldn't trade one for the whole of
Russia. Literally wouldn't. But the thing about
kids is to give them an intelligent break—know
what makes them tick. And I'm letting *my* children
understand what goes on in their country—not
bringing them up in some crazy dream world.
They face hard facts.

Of course, you've got to have an understanding
of child psychology. And you can't be ambitious. I
want my children to be normal kids, in every way.
Come the revolution, I want them to go out and
take their place shoulder to shoulder with the
masses of people. I'm watching it already, keeping
my finger right on it. In the first place, I don't let
my kids see too much of me. Why? Simply because
I don't want them to become precocious. In school,
I never urge them to go after perfect marks. Never!
I want 80's. No 90's, no 100's, in my family. They

learn to be democratic, too, by God. In my house
there's no darn little aristocrats running around,
I'll tell the world. My wife and I not only let the
children play with their inferiors, but we en-
courage it. Why, only last week I saw one of my
youngsters playing around with the laundress's
kid. Why shouldn't he, for heaven's sake? I suppose
the neighbors think we're crazy, but what do we
care?

And money! That's where so many people go
wrong in relation to children. Take Christmas.
Fortunately situated though I am, I insisted on a
completely frugal Christmas last December. I
mapped out the entire occasion, and put it
through. Each of the children received exactly
three presents—one gift that they wanted, one gift
that they would learn something from, and one
gift that they didn't know existed. All other presents, from outside sources, my wife and I confis-
cated in advance and distributed to the poor.
Furthermore, my kids did their own shopping—
actually bought the things they were to give us out
of their own allowance. Of course, Mamselle went
with them to the shops, but they did the selecting.

In that way they got the true meaning of Christmas. They presented me with the god-damnedest ash trays you ever saw, but listen: I have those ashtrays sitting right on my desk at the office, and I'll be looking at them the rest of my life, and loving it. Oh, I don't fool myself about children. Nobody knows better than I do that you can't plan their lives for them. If one of my boys wants to become a railway conductor, I'll be the first to say Go to it. Matter of fact, I imagine my oldest lad is heading for journalism. Guess he comes by it honestly, as far as that goes. I've always been able to pick up a paper and get the meat out of it. Just a glance at this edition is enough. Just a question of stripping a thing down to its essentials. Foreign news—all disguised these days. Have to read between th' lines. These Fascist powers. Inter'sting. Inter'sting to an executive, p'ticularly. Triumph of efficient organization. Man like Mussolini: threat to our traditional notions, perhaps; not above criticism, perhaps; but magnificent in victory. Nothing clumsy about that kind of government. He doesn't ask 'em, he tells 'em. That's thing England can't understand. This man Van Zeeland. Includes England as one of the great powers in his plan for economic c'llaboration. Big mistake to include England. England hardly need be considered any more, strength so far diss'pated. I would like another drink—would you mind pushing that button just behind your head? Thank you very much.

Philip Wedge

To the friends of Philip Wedge, his gradual withdrawal from human society was the cause of some wonderment. Most of them were bothered less by his having renounced the world than by their not knowing why. One explanation was that he had taken up with a woman. A few people said money had something to do with it.

Both explanations were absurd. I knew Wedge well, and got wind of some of the little matters that eventually drove him into a kind of retirement. For one thing, he had a curious feeling in regard to his nose, being often troubled with the suspicion that there was a black smudge on the side of it. This suspicion was usually groundless, but used to attack him suddenly, unsettling him and causing him embarrassment and physical discomfort. I have seen him, dining with a large company, twist quickly in his chair and point questioningly at his nose. Assured by the person next to him that the nose was spotless, he would remain uneasy and would close first one eye, then the other, in an

attempt to peer downward and sideways at the
suspected member. After almost throwing his eye-
balls out of their sockets, he would dip his nap-
kin fiercely in a tumbler and dab hard at his nose,
reddening it and surprising the whole company.

That was only one thing that troubled him. He
was also subject to the suspicion that he had
feathers on his back. One of a group of persons in
a drawing-room, he would without warning throw
his right hand desperately over his left shoulder,
and flick at his back, in real terror. This feeling was
not without some basis in fact, for at one time the
pillow in his bed had developed a leak and for a
period of about a week he had found feathers here
and there on his person. The pillow had been dis-
carded, of course, but he seemed unable to forget
the feathers, and never could believe he was quite
without them.

Wedge had difficulty keeping appointments—a
failing which further explains his reclusion. He
was at heart a romantic fellow and had built up a
strange myth about the telephone: he could not
bear to think of its ringing when he was not there
to answer it, lest the message be one which might
change the whole course of his life. His modest

apartment was on the fourth floor, and he once told me that he never left it—to keep a date or for any other reason—but that he felt, after shutting the door, that the phone was ringing. Sometimes the suspicion did not take hold of him until he was down three flights of stairs, when he would turn and spring like a goat back up the stairs, fumble madly with his key, and burst into the room to find all quiet. Often this furious ascent would so derange his clothes that he would have to make a complete change, and once or twice, he confided, it had so exhausted him that he had to lie down.

I can't help thinking that Wedge's pet turtle had something to do with his taking the veil. He kept the little beast in an old photograph-developer pan, and fed it bits of beef which he brought from restaurants as often as he remembered to. Unfortunately, he had never devised a satisfactory method of carrying the morsels home, but almost invariably wrapped them in his handkerchief when he thought no one was looking, and replaced the handkerchief in his hip-pocket. This would have been a decent enough expedient had Wedge always gone directly home from the restaurant, but frequently he was diverted, and I happen to know of several occasions when he pulled out his handkerchief—in the lobby of a theatre, in a club, in a cab—and out dropped beef on the floor. Rather than admit to owning a turtle, Wedge preferred to let the matter stand without any explanation; but it unnerved him, and people never understood.

He was a nervous person, anyway. I recall (now that I'm thinking about these things) a day, probably three years ago, when he and I were walking together down Sixth Avenue. As we passed a letter-box, Wedge dropped a letter in—a slight incident which I thought nothing of until, a block later, Wedge suddenly turned and darted back along the sidewalk, twisting and turning and looking from the rear very like a madman. When he reached the letter-box, he seized the slot and jiggled it viciously a dozen times, glancing in finally to see that it was empty. When he joined me again he seemed tired and spent. He told me, in a jerky, shy manner, that he frequently was bothered by the fear that his letter had not been properly posted, and found it necessary to rush back and make sure that it had dropped all the way down into the box.

I shall not call up all Wedge's peculiarities; yet I can hardly omit mention of his phobia about oranges and grapefruit. He delighted in the taste of citrus fruits, and preferred to eat them with a spoon rather than drink the juice; yet I know for a fact that he could not get halfway through an orange without imagining that he had swallowed a pit. The moment this thought took hold of him, he laid down his spoon and puckered his throat into a bad knot, trying to reclaim the imaginary object from his esophagus. This set him against oranges and disturbed his digestion. When other persons were present at table, their astonishment increased his agony.

For all the absurdity of these fears, I suspect Wedge would still not have isolated himself from society had it not been for another peculiarity of his—which I shall explain as delicately as I can. (He told me the main facts himself, so I am not guessing.) At various times in his life, Wedge had courted ladies, with rather a positive grace for so excitable a man. And of course, in going about, he had had occasion to kiss many of them—which he managed with more amiability than passion. By dint of confining his affectionate regard to one lady at a time, and to none very long, he managed to come through his affairs with no very great re-

morse or embarrassment. Shortly before his renun-
ciation of society, he was kissing a fine woman in a
perfectly creditable manner when (possibly as a
result of a phrase he had read somewhere and remembered) the suspicion overcame him that his
consort had opened her eyes, in the midst of the
kiss, and was calmly regarding him. There was no
way definitely to confirm or disprove the suspicion,
for Wedge felt that he was ethically unwarranted
in opening his own eyes, as well as biologically in-
capable of it. Therefore, the suspicion remained to
trouble him and make all further companionship
with the opposite sex unthinkable.

He now lives quietly with his turtle. By divorc-
ing his friends he has probably added to his tranquillity; and I suspect he hasn't changed much but
still goes about dabbing his nose, whacking feathers from his back, rushing upstairs to a silent and
scornful telephone, jiggling letter-boxes, choking
over his orange, and pulling from his hip-pocket a
handkerchief from which falls a little morsel of
beef. I rather liked him.

The Street of the Dead

WHEN THEY CAME TO ELEVENTH STREET, ON THEIR way to school, the little boy said to his father, "Is this the street with the graveyard?"

"Yes," said the man.

"Can we go through it, please, so I can see the graveyard?"

"Let's go through Twelfth Street," said the man, "and I'll show you a house I used to live in years ago."

"I want to see the graveyard with dead people." He pulled at his father's hand, and as was often the case with the man and his four-year-old, the little boy got his way—not by being rude or obstreperous but by a certain superior force of character, a certain intensity. They turned into Eleventh Street. The man realized that he had given in, but he half suspected that in such a matter the child had a right to his own prejudices.

The father rather enjoyed these early morning trips to school. The dog always went along, a sturdy

black animal with an idiot love of life. They made
an odd trio, the dog tugging hard at the leash; the
little boy, hampered by thick leggings, dragging
behind; the man a twisted but happy link between
them, letting the dog supply the motive power for
all three—swept through the chill winter streets
at a quarter to nine, the man's hastily swallowed
breakfast not sitting any too well, his eyes not yet
focussing clearly.

"Is that it?" cried the little boy, breaking into a
gallop. "Look, Daddy, there's a grave!" They had
arrived at the tiny cemetery near Sixth Avenue, a
triangular plot where two or three underfed trees
sheltered the sparse dead of the Spanish and Portuguese Synagogue. Dreary above the hard-packed
mud rose the headstones; between them lay some
fragments of broken glass and old candy wrappers.
A cat moved slowly along the brick wall at the rear.

"There's another grave!" cried the child, his
cheeks pressed against the iron bars of the gate.

"Look at that big ol' cat up there on the wall,"
said the man. "That's some cat!"

"Is it dead?" asked the little boy.

"No, it's alive," said the man. Then he added:
"Alive and well."

"If I died would they put me in?"

"You're not going to."

"Would they bury me?"

"Yes. We better hurry or we'll be late for school." The child hugged the iron gate tightly; his grip was strong.

"If I fell out of our window would I die?"

The man calculated the vertical distance, saw the toppling child, saw the fall, the crowd, the pavement, the people staring, saw the report of the ambulance surgeon.

"Yes," he replied. "Come along now, son."

They pulled away. The dog whirled them on, out of danger, into life again. They crossed over the street, and up a block, and over to school. The man went in with his son and accompanied him up three or four flights of stairs to the play yard on the roof. He stood for a moment in the doorway, talking to the teacher. She was a short woman, with a kind heart and flashing eyes.

"We're very enthusiastic about Elliott," she said.

"So am I," said the man, absently.

"At first he had a tendency toward over-stimulation, but he's beautifully adjusted now."

"That's good," said the man, who was having a little trouble with the dog.

"Elliott really makes such good use of his information," she continued.

"His information?" echoed the man, dreamily. He watched his son pick up a wooden block and heave it.

"We try to direct all their little energies toward inventive things, so that they have an immediate creative object. You see, children have a tendency to try to solve social situations."

"They do?"

"Yes, and that's bad."

"Of course."

"We have one little girl here, and at first she was interested only in tackling adult problems and social situations. She doesn't happen to be here today with the group—she strained her knee playing, and the doctor said she might as well stay home, because it hinders her in Rhythms."

"That's too bad," said the man.

"It's wonderful how she has come around, I mean about not trying to solve social situations. But children are like that. It's just a question of getting at them and knowing what they're all about."

"I suppose it is."

He said goodbye, his eyes lingering on his son for a parting look. Led by the idiot dog, he scrambled downstairs and out into the street. He put on his hat, jerked it down over his eyes, started for home at a fast clip, no little boy dragging this time. Homeward journeys were made in record time, the dog in high. It was just a question of getting back to the apartment, slipping the leash, taking another sip of cold coffee, gathering up the newspaper, and starting uptown to work. At the corner of Eleventh the dog, remembering the cat in the cemetery, pulled hard, trying to force a turn into the block. The man yanked back. "Come on!" he muttered angrily. The dog continued to strain, the collar gagging him.

"Come on, come on, you crazy bastard!"

The man jerked the protesting animal along; and together they went home, through Tenth, each wrapped darkly in his own thoughts.